KU-490-051

The Great Intellectual Revolution

The Great Intellectual Revolution

J . F . WEST

The Great Intellectual

Revolution

JOHN MURRAY

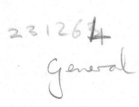

C

2312634

General

© J. F. West 1965

Printed in Great Britain by
Cox & Wyman Ltd., London, Fakenham and Reading
and published by John Murray (Publishers) Ltd
50 Albemarle Street, London W.1

UNIVERSITY
LIBRARY
NOTTINGHAM

Foreword

This book is an attempt to step over the boundaries of all 'subjects', and to consider the inter-relatedness of things. Studies today become specialized at an extraordinarily early stage. This is not necessarily a bad thing, but it is useful, even from a narrowly specialist viewpoint, to step back and see life in the round.

Particularly valuable for students of all subjects is the study of that key period, the seventeenth century. For the origins of the 'gaps' between the various disciplines of learning, and the great gulf between the sciences and the arts, must be sought in that century. This book attempts to show the relevance of the growth of science to the history of literature, for instance; and to give a historical perspective to the student of science. It tries to show how the growth of science, the political history of the times, the changes in literary expression, and the philosophies put forward, were all inter-related and interacting, and both produced and responded to a climate of opinion which was changing so radically during the course of the century as to amount to an intellectual revolution, perhaps the most important in human history, and one which is still far from complete.

This book has no pretensions to impartiality. The writer has taken no precautions against letting his own prejudices declare themselves when he is interpreting the course of events, in the view that the purposes of the book are better achieved by vigour than by a colourless noncommittal attitude. Footnotes and references are not to be found, as the book is not meant as a primer in the history of science. Rather, it is intended as an aid towards a more comprehensive understanding of studies in the arts or the sciences.

Mankind has passed through at least three periods of revolutionary change in his way of life since he became recognizably man. The first was the Neolithic Revolution, when agriculture, carried out with the help of implements of polished stone, spread from some focus in the Middle East about 6000 BC, together with such basic crafts as spinning, weaving and pottery. This revolution enabled men to live closer to one another, and the field of human co-operation was vastly extended. The second was the Literary Revolution, when writing was invented. Through writing, permanency was brought to human experience. Man was no longer dependent on the memory of the old men, remembering what other old men had once told them in their youth, for tapping the intellectual resources of the past. Such social operations as law-giving and tax-collecting became immeasurably easier, and higher forms of religion and literature became possible. The third period of revolutionary change, which I have called the Great Intellectual Revolution, is still going on.

Any sketch of the Great Intellectual Revolution must be a very partial one. Its timing was determined by a host of factors, such as advances in metallurgy, the spread of good methods of paper-making (which made printing an economic proposition), and the discovery, or rediscovery, of America. Its effects, too, have been far too large in scale to be chronicled in a single book. It seems astonishing that in fewer than three hundred years, by conscious and systematic endeavour, human skill should move from the crude springs and pumps of Hooke to the complexities of a nuclear power station of today. Equally astonishing, in our own time, will be the spread of the Revolution to that majority of the world's lands which have so far been almost untouched by it.

This book is concerned chiefly with intellectual and theoretical issues, and their relationship to the world at large. This is, in the first place, because the process of intellectual change is in itself interesting. Also, for many purposes, it is useful to know what men's basic assumptions were before and after the change. Much remains with us from pre-revolutionary times which is of extreme value – the plays of Shakespeare, the common law, the whole continuity of the old with the new, basic religious and ethical concepts of human conduct. These ought to be viewed in the light of the great revolution in human ideas. It is useful, too, to observe the rise of ideas which are now so essential to our thinking that it requires an effort of the imagination to realize that they are not self-evident.

It may be useful to summarize briefly, at this stage, the main features of the change in human ideas which took place in the seventeenth century. They were as follows:

(*a*) The known universe became suddenly vaster, and man's home was no longer at its centre.

(*b*) Educated men began to expect to find the world working like a machine, without constant divine or diabolical interference.

(*c*) Educated men began to expect to find the truth about phenomena through mathematical methods, and through inductive processes.

(*d*) Occult effects were no longer looked for. (Divinity ceased to hedge kings, for instance.) A utilitarian attitude began to grow.

(*e*) The distinction became much clearer between words and things. It became recognized that much traditional learning had been the mere giving of new names, instead of the recognition of relationships.

(*f*) A new appreciation sprang up of the skill of the craftsman, and an alliance was formed between artisan and scientist.

(*g*) Analogy and metaphor lost status, and in consequence, prose tended to replace poetry as the vehicle of serious writing.

(*h*) It became accepted that if there was any apparent conflict between truth and an aspect of morality, the truth must nevertheless be published.

Many people did not like the world-picture which began to take shape as the century advanced. They struggled hard to maintain many values which seemed inextricably tied up with the old points of view. But no one could ignore the new discoveries and retain any intellectual honesty. Much more in these days, as we reap the material benefits of the intellectual revolution, we have to reconcile ourselves to the hard task of maintaining many non-material, but essentially human values, without retreating from established facts.

Contents

Acknowledgements

The author and publishers are indebted to the following for permission to reproduce copyright photographs:

Messrs Colin Ronan Ltd (Plates 1, 3, 4, 5, and 6; Figs 1.1, 1.2, 2.8, 2.9, 2.12, 3.1 redrawn, 5.1 and 7.1); Deutsches Museum (Plate 2); Science Museum (Plate 7 – Crown copyright reserved).

Plates

(between pages 52 and 53)

ONE

Everything in its place

The older type of school history book used to give the impression that there was a great watershed in human affairs around the end of the fifteenth century. The three great events ushering in modern times, and finally closing down the Middle Ages, were supposed to be the Battle of Bosworth Field in 1485, the discovery of America by Columbus in 1492, and the discovery of a sea route to India by Vasco da Gama in 1499. The Reformation, it seemed, consummated these world-shaking events by purifying religion and ending superstition.

Yet in reality one of the most surprising things about the Tudor Reformation is how few basic religious or philosophical beliefs were changed. There was a change of emphasis rather than content. Church government, of course, came in for a thorough reform. The monasteries and chantries of England were dissolved, and the proceeds spent or invested by king and courtiers. But the beliefs of educated men remained much as they had been before. The world picture emerging from the works of Shakespeare (1564–1616) has a remarkable amount in common with that of Chaucer (c.1340–1400). The climate of ideas in which Jonathan Swift (1667–1745) wrote, on the other hand, is as plainly close to that of today. It was the seventeenth century, not the sixteenth, in which modern times began. Backward countries of today lose their backwardness (at least intellectually) as they adopt the ideas which became current in western Europe, especially in England, in the seventeenth century. The seventeenth century was the age of the Great Intellectual Revolution.

That Revolution took place principally as a result of scientific discovery. Before 1600, men searching for truth would look to the writings of the ancients; after 1700, reason and experiment were held to be the crucial test of truth. There was, moreover, an increasing use of mathematics; and of the *inductive* method, which derives generalizations from a large number of instances, rather than the *deductive* method, which derives laws of nature from supposedly unquestionable axioms. Men of learning also turned their attention towards the hitherto ignored work of the blacksmith, the dyer, the sailor, the farmer and the gunner. The process of change, naturally, took a long time: it would be possible to draw a chain of causes from well back in medieval times to explain just why human thought should re-crystallize in the latter part of the seventeenth century; and by 1700, the revolution had still affected only a tiny minority of learned men in a few favoured countries. But it is by the scientific discoveries of the seventeenth century that our most deep-seated assumptions today are governed. Isaac Newton is perhaps the most outstanding figure in the whole history of thought, and he has had a profound and permanent influence on politics, religion, literature, economics, and every other aspect of human behaviour. For human life does not divide itself into compartments, like the subjects in a school timetable. Rather it is like a net, to lift one knot of which is to lift a whole complex of threads.

The ideas of what the world was like, which both Shakespeare and Chaucer understood, were based on a synthesis of the theology of Christianity with the scientific beliefs of some of the ancient Greek authors, particularly Aristotle. St Thomas Aquinas (1225–74) had harmonized the physics of Aristotle, the astronomy of Ptolemy, the medicine of

Galen, into one vast system serving the 'queen of sciences', theology. The Thomist system, although scholars might argue about this detail or that, explained everything, turned all human learning to the glory of God, and provided a satisfying framework on which, it seemed, any new discovery might be hung (see Plate 1).

Knowledge of God, which was the supreme aim of learning, was to be attained both through reason and through revelation. The existence of God was deduced logically in many ways, of which two were particularly favoured. One was the Great First Cause argument, that everything in the universe which moves is observed to have a mover. Push back the inquiry far enough, and one is compelled to assume an Unmoved Mover, which is God. The other was a variety of the so-called 'ontological' argument, deducing God from human intellect. Man is able to conceive of a perfect being; but since the concept of perfection includes perfect existence (since an existent perfect being is more perfect than a non-existent one), this perfect being (God) must exist. The perfect goodness, the omniscience and omnipotence of God could likewise be deduced through the pure processes of logic. It seems that the first philosopher to advance this second argument was St Anselm (1033–1109); and as we shall see, the important seventeenth-century philosopher Descartes used it in his short-lived but important system designed to replace that of St Thomas Aquinas.

But it was revelation, not reason, which taught the relationship between God and the world, including man. Revelation was enshrined partly in the Scriptures, and partly in the teaching of the Church, the writings of the early fathers having particular weight. The Roman Catholics tended to emphasize the authority of the Church, the Protestants leaned more heavily on the Bible, but each recognized the need both for scriptures and for authoritative interpreters of scripture.

God's creation included both heaven and earth. Heaven was the home of innumerable hosts of angels, engaged in the love, adoration and imitation of God. A proportion of the angels, said by some writers to be one-third of the total, led by Satan, had revolted against God, and had been thrust out from heaven. Since then, the fallen angels had worked constantly to thwart God's will. When God created Adam and Eve, the machinations of Satan brought about the Fall of Man. The fallen angels abounded in the earth, air, water, and living things. They were adored by the heathens as gods, and even in Christian countries prevailed on men and women to be their conscious and active agents, as sorcerers or witches. Satan also inspired heresies—wrong opinions about God which brought about the damnation of those who held them.

God's will for man, whereby he could redeem himself from the dire effects of the Fall, was made known, first imperfectly and figuratively through the Law and the Prophets, then perfectly through the life and death of Jesus Christ, who was God made Man, and who could thus be a mediator and a divine sacrifice whereby mankind could be reconciled to God. At the Last Day, commonly pictured as being only a few hundred years away, God would judge the living and the dead.

The material world was composed of the four elements: earth, air, fire and water, which combined the four qualities of hotness, coldness, dryness and moistness. Air was hot and wet; fire, hot and dry; earth, cold and dry; water, cold and wet. Natural phenomena were caused by the properties of the elements, for each had its natural place in the universe. Earth, the heaviest and morally basest of the elements,* tended towards the centre of the universe. Water was also naturally heavy, but less so than earth, and its natural place was in a covering over the earth. Fire was

* Shakespeare makes the dying Cleopatra say, 'I am fire and air; my other elements I give to baser life'.

the lightest element, and its natural place was in an invisible belt high above the surface of the earth; where occasionally comets and meteors were formed from its substance. Air tended to a place between the fire and the water. These four elements were never met with in a pure form – actual substances were combinations, more or less tightly compacted.

The distillation of organic substances, or their combustion, seemed to lend confirmation to this theory, in so far as it was regarded as needing confirmation. In Robert Boyle's *The Sceptical Chymist*, the adherent of the old philosophy puts the argument thus:

For if you but consider a piece of green wood burning in a chimney, you will readily discern in the disbanded parts of it the four elements, of which we teach it and other mixed bodies to be composed. The fire discovers itself in the flame by its own light; the smoke by ascending to the top of the chimney, and there readily vanishing into air, like a river losing itself in the sea, sufficiently manifests to what element it belongs and gladly returns. The water in its own form boiling and hissing at both ends of the burning wood betrays itself to more than one of our senses; and the ashes by their weight, their firmness, and their dryness, put it past doubt that they belong to the element of earth.

The pursuit of alchemy naturally followed from this theory of the elements (see Fig. 1.1). Gold was visualized as the perfect compound of the four elements in their perfect proportion. It was therefore a simple deduction that the less perfect metals, such as lead, might be transmuted by a change in proportion between their constituents. As gold was a 'perfect' compound, it must also, if brought to a liquid form, be a universal medicine, because the perfectly healthy man was one in whom the elements were mixed in a perfect proportion.

Motion, apart from the 'natural' motion of the two light elements upwards, and the two heavy elements downwards,

Fig. 1.1 An alchemist's workshop in the sixteenth century. Although there are tools and instruments of many kinds, there is no balance.

was initiated and maintained by some mover. Living beings were able to initiate 'violent' or unnatural movement by virtue of possessing a soul. The principle of inertia, as will be later explained, was simply not understood. It was believed that if the mover stopped pushing the moving object, the object would immediately stop.

The heavenly bodies were pictured as revolving in crystal spheres, round the central and stationary earth. The moon, the lowest and basest of the planets (as witnessed by its dull markings), travelled in the lowest and swiftest sphere, just above the sphere of fire. There followed Mercury, Venus, the Sun, Mars, Jupiter and Saturn, the spheres of which moved progressively slower. These planetary motions, although they appeared complex to human observers, could be resolved into a system of circular motions. For heavenly bodies were composed of a perfect fifth element, with a naturally circular motion. Elements below the moon had straight-line natural motions: which implied that each had a 'contrary' away from which it moved. Heavenly bodies had no 'contraries' – the very circularity of their motions was complete, and expressed nobility – and they were consequently unchangeable and incorruptible. Outside the sphere of Saturn was that of the Fixed Stars, and beyond that the Primum Mobile, the mover of the whole system. Some cosmologists argued also for an 'Intelligence' to each sphere, a divine being charged with maintaining the motion of that planet. Others maintained that there was a Crystalline Sphere between that of the Fixed Stars and the Primum Mobile, which, as will be later mentioned, had the care of a minor correction.

There was, however, fairly general agreement that the heavenly spheres poured forth the most sublime music, which was unfortunately inaudible to human ears. Shakespeare makes Lorenzo say to Jessica, as they sit on a moonlit bank together at the end of *The Merchant of Venice*:

> Look how the floor of heaven
> Is thick inlaid with patines of bright gold;
> There's not the smallest orb which thou behold'st
> But in his motion like an angel sings,
> Still quiring to the young-ey'd cherubims:
> Such harmony is in immortal souls;
> But while this muddy vesture of decay
> Doth grossly close it in, we cannot hear it.

He assumes that it is the admixture of the baser elements to the soul that masks the music, and very wisely had provided his own.

The sun certainly, and the other planets possibly, generated elements outside their natural place in the world. Hence, the actual substances did not separate out into their constituent elements, and fall into layers, but were kept in equilibrium.

Human biology had many points of correspondence with the four-element system, the same four qualities combining in the body to form the so-called humours. Blood combined hotness and wetness; black bile or melancholy combined coldness and dryness; yellow bile or choler combined hotness and dryness; while phlegm combined coldness and wetness. An excess of one or another humour produced a characteristic temperament and characteristic diseases, which might be cured by righting the balance. We still, today, use the terms sanguine, choleric, melancholic and phlegmatic in very much their medieval senses, though the word *humorous* has changed its meaning from temperamental to comic.

The humours were imagined to be produced from the food eaten. Blood was produced in the liver, from the most temperate parts of the chyle, or digested food; its function was to nourish the whole body through the veins and arteries. Phlegm was also produced in the liver, but from the colder part of the chyle; it moistened the naturally moist parts of the body, such as the tongue. Choler was a bitter humour produced from the hottest part of the chyle, and gathered in the gall; it was thought to keep the body warm, and to help in excretion. Melancholy was a thick, black, sour humour which derived from the most turbid part of the chyle, and was produced by the spleen; it nourished the bones, and kept the hot humours, blood and choler, under control. The chyle itself was conceived as being produced from food in the stomach and intestines by a process analagous to cooking.

Blood, the hot and wet humour, had a direct relationship with the element air, and the spring season. Choler likewise was related to fire and summer. Melancholy was related to the earth and autumn, while phlegm was related to water and winter. Now since the sun and the planets were producing elements in the world by their progress through the heavens, there was a natural belief in astrology – the system in which the planets were supposed to affect human health and destiny (see Fig. 1.2). (The Doctor of Physic in

Fig. 1.2 A sixteenth-century illustration showing the influence of the sun, moon and planets on human destiny. From a corpse, on which a crow is sitting, issue the two spirits of Man – the vital spirit and the natural spirit. Between the sun and moon are Venus, Mars, Mercury, Jupiter and Saturn, the last-named black, as befits the planet of evil luck and mourning.

Chaucer's *Canterbury Tales* is described as being an expert astrologer.) A conjunction of Saturn and Jupiter in Libra, or of Saturn and the moon in Scorpio, for instance, was supposed to produce melancholy. It was very generally recognized that astrology and alchemy were favoured fields of swindlers and quacks, and a few voices claimed that both supposed sciences were sheer imagination, when nothing worse. Nevertheless the bulk of sober opinion believed that there was a genuine astrological knowledge to be found, however imperfect man's actual understanding of the celestial processes, and that a physician could not attain a proper grasp of his art without skill in astrology.

Opinion differed on the strength of celestial compulsion. Some scholars regarded the stars as having a direct effect on mankind, which could not be resisted. This was dangerously near the belief in predestination, which only the Calvinists accepted. Others regarded the heavens as inclining events towards one end or another, but not irresistibly. Others again believed that the heavens were a sign of terrestrial events, but not their cause, just as an innkeeper's sign is a symbol, but not a cause, of his business. It was, however, very generally felt fitting that there should be a link between the macrocosm, the universe, and the microcosm, man. The earth-centred astronomy agreed well with the supposition that the heavenly bodies were created for the benefit of the inhabitants of the earth. It could not be supposed that they were there for any other purpose. Everything had to have a purpose.

Everything, too, had its place in the divine order. St Thomas Aquinas said that the universe was a hierarchy of creatures ordered to the attainment of perfection in their several kinds. This hierarchy, or chain of being, was supposed to extend from God, the supreme perfection, down through the angelic orders, to man, the terrestrial creature which alone was capable of reason and of an apprehension of God; next came the animals, from the lion, the eagle and the dolphin (thought of as the noblest of land, air and sea creatures) to the meanest worm; then the plants, which had nutritive powers, but unlike animals, lacked locomotion; and finally the minerals, from gold and the obviously powerful lodestone to the humblest dust. If there was a departure from this natural order, disaster might be expected. Shakespeare expresses this idea very clearly in the speech of Ulysses, in *Troilus and Cressida*. Ulysses is explaining why, after many years of siege, Troy has not fallen: because the authority of the generals is being spurned. 'Degree', or order, is the prime law of nature:

> The heavens themselves, the planets, and this centre
> Observe degree, priority and place,
> Insisture, course, proportion, season, form,
> Office, and custom, all in line of order:
> And therefore is the glorious planet Sol
> In noble eminence enthron'd and spher'd
> Amidst the other; whose medicinable eye
> Corrects the ill aspects of planets evil,
> And posts, like the commandment of a king,
> Sans check, to good and bad: but when the planets
> In evil mixture, to disorder wander,
> What plagues and what portents! what mutiny!
> What raging of the sea! shaking of earth!
> Commotion in the winds! frights, changes, horrors,
> Divert and crack, rend and deracinate
> The unity and married calm of states
> Quite from their fixture . . . the bounded waters
> Should lift their bosoms higher than the shores,
> And make a sop of all this solid globe:
> Strength should be lord of imbecility,
> And the rude son should strike his father dead:
> Force should be right; or rather, right and wrong –
> Between whose endless jar justice resides –
> Should lose their names, and so should justice too.

Disorder in the heavens led to disorder on earth. The same theme runs constantly through the play of *King Lear*, where the tumult of rebellion of child against father is reflected in the tempest.

Degree extended through everything. God, the Creator and Sustainer of the universe, had made all things to communicate Himself more fully. All His creatures had a nature or 'form', the discovery of which constituted human knowledge. Angels were of nine degrees, three each of three orders: Seraphs, Cherubs and Thrones were contemplative by nature; Dominions, Virtues and Powers were thought to be active, but mentally rather than physically; Principalities, Archangels and Angels constituted the active order, which carried out the physical will of God. The lowest rank, of ordinary angels, was the grade which visited man. Mankind as a whole was a little lower than the angels, and could also be classified in ranks from Pope and Emperor down to the poorest beggar.

But man, though below the angelic orders, excelled in one respect. Because he lacked the perfection of knowledge of the angels, he excelled them in the power of learning. Below man were the beasts, who, however, excelled man in their physical powers. The plants excelled the beasts in their power to nourish themselves, a power again arising from a deficiency – the inability to move. Stones, the inanimate order of being, nevertheless excelled plants in strength and durability. A further beauty in the pattern was that the angelic creation, pure life without material, balanced the mineral creation, which was pure material without life, and so on, producing a satisfying symmetry.

Such was the philosophy which was overthrown in the seventeenth century. Because everything had its place, and one part of the system backed up another, the whole ministering to human self-importance, it was only after bitter struggle that mankind could be brought to admit that, for the most part, it was merely words piled on beautiful words. When it was not plainly false, it meant nothing from a physical point of view. It collapsed when men began to weigh and measure.

TWO

The Sun is lost

The Ptolemaic theory of planetary motion, and the Aristotelian theory of mechanics, were the first portions of the traditional world picture to be overthrown – to the great consternation of churchmen and philosophers. It was no accident, moreover, that astronomical and mechanical data should be among the first scientific applications of mathematics. The length of the year, and the positions of the stars and planets had to be determined accurately both for Church purposes (Pope Gregory XIII reformed the calendar in 1582), and for navigation to the newly discovered lands. Likewise, the development of effective artillery, and of systems of fortification which would provide protection against it, created a need to find out exactly how cannonballs did in fact travel, instead of how they 'ought' to travel if their course were to fit the world-picture which men had.

In Marlowe's play, *Doctor Faustus* (1589), the Ptolemaic system, and its theological implications, are described with unusual clarity. Doctor Faustus has just sold his soul to Mephistophilis, Lucifer's deputy, for twenty-four years of power and enjoyment, with Mephistophilis as his servant; and his first demands are for knowledge.

> Faustus: Come, Mephistophilis, let us dispute again,
> And argue of divine astrology.
> Tell me, are there many heavens above the Moon?

Are all celestial bodies but one globe,
As is the substance of this centric earth?

Mephistophilis: As are the elements, such are the spheres,
Mutually folded in each other's orb,
And Faustus,
All jointly move upon one axletree,
Whose terminine is termed the world's
wide pole,
Nor are the names of Saturn, Mars or
Jupiter
Feigned, but are erring stars.

Faustus: But tell me, have they all one motion?
Both *situ* and *tempore*?

Mephistophilis: All jointly move from East to West in four
and twenty hours upon the poles of the
world, but differ in their motion upon the
poles of the zodiac.

Faustus: Tush, these slender trifles Wagner can
decide,
Hath Mephistophilis no greater skill?
Who knows not the double motion of the
planets?
The first is finished in a natural day,
The second thus, as Saturn in thirty years,
Jupiter in twelve, Mars in four, the Sun,
Venus, and Mercury in a year: the Moon
in twenty-eight days. Tush, these are fresh-
men's suppositions; but tell me, hath every
sphere a Dominion or *Intelligentia*?

Mephistophilis: Aye.

Faustus: How many heavens or spheres are there?

Mephistophilis: Nine, the seven planets, the Firmament,
and the Empyrean Heaven.

Faustus: But is there not *Coelum Igneum* and *Christa-
linum*?

Mephistophilis: No, Faustus, they be but fables.

Faustus: Well, resolve me in this question, why have we not conjunctions, oppositions, aspects, eclipses, all at one time, but in some years we have more, in some less?

Mephistophilis: *Per inæqualem motum respectu totius.**

Faustus: Well, I am answered; tell me, who made the world?

Mephistophilis: I will not.

Faustus: Sweet Mephistophilis, tell me.

Mephistophilis: Move me not, for I will not tell thee.

Faustus: Villain, have I not bound thee to tell me anything?

Mephistophilis: Aye, that is not against our kingdom, but this is.
Think thou on hell, Faustus, for thou art damned.

In this one passage, we may see not only the details of the astronomical beliefs of the time, but also how these were bound up with physics and theology. Faustus's first question is of the *substance* of which the heavenly bodies are composed. Are they of one substance like the earth, or several? Mephistophilis replies that just as the elements are in layers (earth beneath, then water, air and fire), so are the celestial spheres, although they all move on one axis, through the earth's poles. When Faustus asks whether each sphere has a Dominion or an Intelligence, there is a reference to physics and theology, as well as to astronomy. It will be remembered that a central point in Aristotle's laws of motion was that nothing moved without a mover. Here, the daily motion from east to west is caused by the motion of the poles of the world, but the second motion by an angel (*Dominion* in Christian theology, *Intelligence* in ancient philosophy), according to Mephistophilis. The seven planets thus each

* By the inequality of their movement in reference to the whole.

had a 'heaven'; the Firmament was needed for the stars and as an abode for the angel turning the whole system once a day; and the Empyrean (Imperial in some texts) Heaven enclosed the whole; nine heavens in all (see Plate 2).

Faustus's question about the Sphere of Fire (supposed to lie just below the moon's sphere, and to be transparent), and the Crystalline Sphere (a supernumerary between the Firmament and the Empyrean Heaven, to account for the slow change known as the Precession of the Equinoxes) refers to two details of the astronomical picture which were much disputed. Mephistophilis comes out in favour of simplicity. One wonders why Faustus should have asked the next question, why the heavenly phenomena were irregular, to get the obvious reply that it is through the unequal motion of the heavenly bodies in respect of the whole – for Mephistophilis's description of the celestial motions in his second reply implies this. There is less wonder, in view of the climate of ideas in the sixteenth century, that he should be led from cosmology to creation, and the Creator.

The problem which scholarship had to solve was that the planets had such irregular courses through the sky compared with the so-called fixed stars. For the 'double motion of the planets' is, we now know, really a triple motion, the resultant of the daily rotation of the earth (which affects the fixed stars also), the yearly passage of the earth round the sun, and the orbit of the planet in question, also round the sun, and either faster or slower than the earth's. The apparent course of a planet, against the background of fixed stars, is a series of loops rather like this:

Fig. 2.1

In order to 'save the appearances', Aristotle had followed

two earlier astronomers, Eudoxus and Callipus, in suppos-
ing that *each* planet was set in a *system* of transparent spheres,
each fitting inside the next, all having a regular circular
motion, but at different angular speeds, and with their
axes set in different places, as shown in Fig. 2.2.

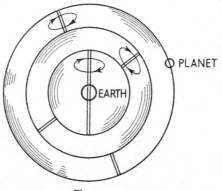

Fig. 2.2

The disadvantages of this system had been felt by most
astronomers to be overwhelming, long before the seventeenth
century, although the extreme defenders of Aristotle's
philosophy were prepared to uphold this too. The trouble
was that each of the seven planets needed a whole nest of
spheres to account for its observed motion, and every
refinement of observation added to that number. Counter-
spheres were needed between each planet's system and the
next, to prevent the motion of one planet being transferred
to its neighbour. The thing was absurdly uneconomical in
celestial crystal, and it was felt that God was probably not
working in this way.

Ptolemy's astronomy assumed that each planet moved
in a circular orbit imposed on a circular orbit – an epicycle.
The centre of a small circle moved evenly round a centre
which was at, or near, the centre of the earth, as in Fig. 2.3.

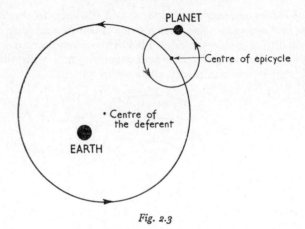

Fig. 2.3

The disadvantages of this system were far fewer, and in
fact, the apparent motions of the planets were represented
with fair accuracy.* When the Pope was reforming the
calendar in 1582, it was a matter of indifference which
system of astronomy he used, Ptolemy's or Copernicus's.
In fact he used the former, as the more familiar.

The suggestion that the sun, not the earth, might be the
centre of the universe, had been advanced in antiquity by
Aristarchus of Samos (third century BC), but had not found

---

* In the interests of clarity, Ptolemy's system has here been slightly
simplified. In addition to the centres of the epicycle and the deferent,
Ptolemy supposed yet another centre, the *equant*. This was the point
from which uniform angular velocity of the centre of the epicycle might
be observed. The purpose of introducing the equant was to bring
uniformity to the variable velocities of the planets. Copernicus detested
the equant, and thought it a great triumph that his system did not need
it. It must be remembered, of course, that in addition to the complexities of deferent, epicycle and equant, the entire planetary system
was moving from east to west daily round a static earth. Alphonso the
Wise of Castile is reputed to have said, after being introduced to the
Ptolemaic system, 'If the Almighty had consulted me before the Creation, I should have recommended something simpler.'

favour even in ancient times, because it could not show
the motion of the planets to be uniform and circular. The
true courses of the planets round the sun are ellipses, with
the sun at one focus; so that attempts to explain their
apparent movements by systems of circles were bound to
break down when once the instruments existed to plot the
data accurately, even though the sun was made the centre.
A half-way heliocentric system had been advanced by
Heraclides of Pontus (fourth century BC), which assumed
that Venus and Mercury revolved round the sun, and the
sun and the outer planets revolved round the earth; but
this was open to the same objections. All the same, when
Copernicus revived the sun-centred theory, he was able to
point out several important respects in which the facts
could be better explained on this basis.

Nicholas Copernicus (1473–1543) was a cleric, educated
at Cracow University, who settled at Frauenburg in East
Prussia, to a busy life as priest, scholar and civil servant.
He was a talented mathematician, and working on the
published data, some of which were far from accurate, and
a few observations of his own, he elaborated a sun-centred
system of astronomy which, though not without drawbacks,
had distinct advantages over the Ptolemaic system. He did
not, as is often thought, eliminate epicycles (in fact he used
slightly more than Ptolemy had thought necessary) because
he too was assuming regular circular motion for bodies
actually moving at varying speeds on elliptical courses;
but he explained facts which Ptolemy had left unexplained.

Since the apparent motion of the planets against the
stellar background is compounded of the earth's motion
round the sun and the planetary motion round the sun,
the apparent motion of the sun is bound to enter into any
calculation of where in the sky a planet is to be expected.
For the inner planets, Mercury and Venus, the Ptolemaic
theory supposed that, for no apparent reason, the centres of
their epicycles were always in line with the sun, as the planets

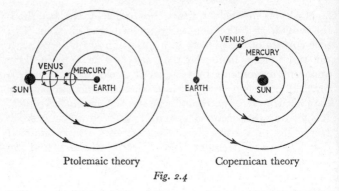

Ptolemaic theory   Copernican theory

Fig. 2.4

were never more than a certain angular distance from the
sun. Copernicus explained why, as can be seen from Fig.2.4.

The apparent motion of the outer planets had a more
subtle connection with the earth–sun relation. It was found
that the line joining the planet to the centre of its epicycle,
on the Ptolemaic theory, was always parallel to the line
joining the earth to the sun (Fig. 2.5). This, too, the Coper-

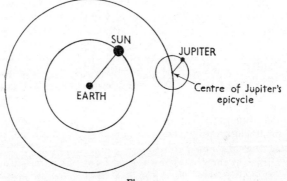

Fig. 2.5

nican theory explained easily, while again the Ptolemaic
theory could only record the fact or evade its implications

by occult arguments about the primacy of the sun among the planets, in the chain of being.

A further advantage of the Copernican theory was that it explained the relative brightness of the planets more satisfactorily than did the Ptolemaic theory. Under the Copernican theory it is easy to see why planets, especially those having orbits near to that of the earth, should vary tremendously in apparent brightness. The distance from earth to planet varies, in the cases of Mercury, Venus and Mars, by an enormous proportion. Ptolemy's epicycles could account for only slight changes of brightness.

Copernicus was also able to predict that sometimes the planets Mercury and Venus would not in fact be seen passing in front of the sun, although the Ptolemaic theory would expect a transit (Fig. 2.6). The phases of Venus and

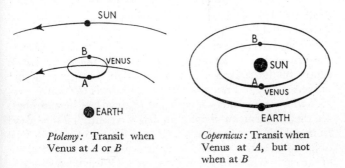

Ptolemy: Transit when Venus at *A* or *B*

Copernicus: Transit when Venus at *A*, but not when at *B*

Fig. 2.6

Mercury, too, could be predicted on the Copernican system, but not on the Ptolemaic (Fig. 2.7).

The objections to Copernicus were many and strong. The strongest argument, to our modern way of thinking, was the absence of an observed stellar parallax, a point which will be dealt with in detail later. At the moment, it is sufficient to observe that Copernicus had to assume

c

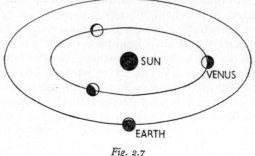

Fig. 2.7

enormous distances between the fixed stars and the earth –
so enormous as to be incredible to most fair-minded
astronomers of the time, though small enough compared
with what we now know them to be. But the main objections
dealt with physical assumptions taken from other parts of
Aristotle's philosophy.

For instance, the earth was supposed to be the centre of
the universe, and heavy things naturally fell towards the
centre of the universe. If the sun were the centre of the
universe, why did not the earth fall towards the sun?

Again, a stone thrown up into the air might be expected,
on the Copernican theory, to fall westward of the place
from which it was thrown. If a follower of Copernicus
objected that the stone, when thrown up, kept the motion
of the earth which it had at the moment it was thrown up, it
was easy to reply, using the Aristotelian dictum that motion
stopped when there was no longer any impressed force, that
as soon as the stone left the earth it could no longer partake
of the earth's motion. Nothing moved, said Aristotle,
unless it had a mover. So the earth would move on, and the
stone be left. As this was not observed, and as birds seemed
to be in no difficulty, the earth must be still.

There was not unnaturally a preference for keeping the
earth at the centre of the universe, and unmoved, since

there was no consciousness of movement by the inhabitants of the earth, and it was felt more dignified that the earth should occupy a unique position. Some based their objections to Copernicus on the belief that the earth would shake to pieces, or that water would fly from the globe, like waterdrops from a wheel, through the swiftness of such a terrestrial motion. From a geometrical point of view, the two systems were equivalent, and either could be used for drawing up navigation tables – the Copernican being perhaps somewhat easier to use.

It is remarkable that the views of Copernicus, which became known through the scholarly world from about 1540 onwards, should during the whole of the sixteenth century have roused no violent opposition. Luther and Calvin both rejected the sun-centred hypothesis, but did not think it worth making a big issue of their rejection. The learned world began to get nervous only as it became increasingly obvious that Copernicus was right, in general pattern if not in detail. Theological issues were at stake as well as scientific ones. For instance, if the earth was but one among many inhabited worlds, as now seemed likely to some Copernicans, the divine scheme of redemption would need to be repeated in many places, which for various reasons was theologically unacceptable. The mere rotation of the earth, opposed as it is to the literal interpretation of many biblical texts, was hard enough to accept. In such circumstances, as long as the evidence is not overwhelming, the reaction of the religious conservative tends to be to deny the new hypothesis, and to impugn the evidence for it. This happened over Copernicanism.

In 1610, the Italian mathematician and astronomer Galileo (1564–1642) observed the phases of Venus through the newly invented telescope. He also was able to observe and measure the change in the apparent size of the planetary discs, and his figures agreed with the Copernican calculations, not with any form of the Ptolemaic theory. Moreover, he observed a model of the solar system in the satellites of Jupiter – bodies it was impossible to fit into the Ptolemaic theory.

Despite the dismissal by Marlowe's Mephistophilis of the sphere of fire just below the moon's sphere, most philosophers before 1600 believed in it,* and supposed that comets were formed from it, while the heavens were unchanging and incorruptible. Galileo was far from popular when he proved that some comets were more distant than the sun, and that the sun, indeed, the most noble of the planets, had spots. Comets, it seemed, were always more distant than the moon. These observations, together with the appearance of 'new stars' in 1572 and 1604, were a serious inconvenience to the traditional astronomy.

Public opinion was very shocked. The Roman Catholic Church managed to silence Galileo (who had been somewhat incautious in expressing his view on the theological implications of his work), but his ideas were already abroad, and their truth was only too patent. John Donne, the English poet and dean of St Paul's, an adherent of the traditional learning, saw the political, as well as the religious implications of these discoveries. He wrote:

> And New Philosophy calls all in doubt,
> The element of Fire is quite put out;
> The Sun is lost, and th'Earth, and no man's wit
> Can well direct him where to look for it.
> And freely men confess that this world's spent,
> When in the Planets, and the Firmament
> They seek so many new; then see that this
> Is crumbled out again to his atomies.
> 'Tis all in pieces, all coherence gone;
> All just supply, and all relation:

* So did Shakespeare. In *Antony and Cleopatra*, Mark Antony says, before a land and sea engagement, 'I would they'd fight i' the fire or i' the air.' This makes good strategic sense on the theory that there are concentric spheres of air and fire above the earth.

Prince, subject, father, son are things forgot,
For every man alone thinks he hath got
To be a phoenix, and that then can be
None of that kind, of which he is, but he.
(Anatomy of the World)

The civil and ecclesiastical order, Donne felt, was shattered by the new truths discovered. In this, he was extraordinarily astute, for the traditional geocentric astronomy fitted well with royal and episcopal power. The new astronomy involved a complete rejection of Aristotle and the scholastic approach, a willingness to question traditional values, to submit problems to the test of measurement. As a recent historian has pointed out, the Cavalier party contained all the notable followers of Ptolemy, and the Roundheads all the Copernicans.

Yet although Galileo's observations were sufficient to refute Ptolemaic astronomy, the Copernican astronomy had still not been set on its full mathematical basis. It became possible to deduce the true courses of the planets, only after the work of a wealthy Danish eccentric, Tycho Brahe (1546–1601), one of the greatest astronomers of all time. He early realized that the traditional data used in astronomical theory were far from exact. He therefore set himself the task of precise measurement of the apparent positions of celestial bodies. He used family influence with the King of Denmark to gain feudal control of the island of Hveen in the Sound, and a grant of sufficient money to set up his famous observatory of Uraniborg. The telescope had not yet been invented, but he built enormous brass quadrants and globes, with accurate scales and sighting devices. For thirty years, in Denmark and in Prague, he undertook systematic observations on the heavenly bodies. Whereas Copernicus had attempted to represent the positions of the planets to within ten minutes of arc – one-sixth of a degree – Tycho regularly made his measurements to an accuracy of two minutes, or even half a minute of arc. He observed the

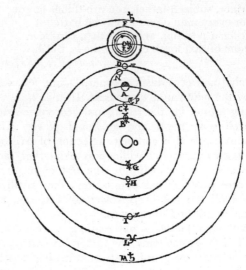

Fig. 2.8 The planetary system of Copernicus, as put forward by
Galileo in 1632.

new star of 1572, and proved that it must lie beyond the
planets. He was the first to suggest that comets moved on
oval orbits, and that these orbits passed through the solid
celestial spheres, if such things existed.

Tycho Brahe rejected the idea that the earth was moving
– by nature and by family tradition he was conservative –
but his theory was the nearest possible to it. He believed
that the sun, moon, and fixed stars revolved round the
stationary earth, while the planets described orbits round
the moving sun. Venus and Mercury had smaller orbits
round the sun, than the sun had round the earth, while
Mars, Jupiter and Saturn had larger orbits. Thus the latter
planets might be seen anywhere in the sky, but the former
only near the sun, for a few hours before sunrise or sunset.
(Cf. Figs. 2.8 and 2.9, and see Plate 3.)

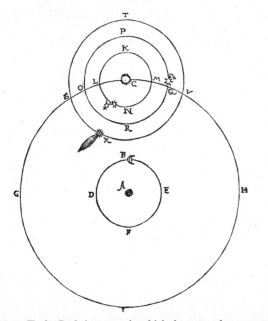

Fig. 2.9 Tycho Brahe's system, in which the sun and moon went round the fixed earth, while the planets, and a comet, circle the sun. Here only Mercury and Venus are shown. The orbit of one outer planet can be seen in the representation in Plate 3.

There was much to be said for this compromise, which was widely accepted through the learned world, because from the time Copernicus had first published his theory, his opponents had remarked on the absence of stellar parallax. If one walks round in a circle in the middle of a room, objects round the room change their apparent relative positions.* But the stars appear to keep precisely to their

* On the assumption that the stars were scattered through space, a change in relative position (parallax) was to be looked for. On the assumption that the stars were all at equal distances from the earth, one expected to observe more space between stars if one was nearer.

places – hence their name of 'fixed stars'. The explanation is, of course, that the stars are such enormous distances from the earth that the parallax cannot easily be observed, even with delicate instruments (see Fig. 2.10). H. H. Spencer Jones, the late Astronomer Royal, gave a vivid picture of the problem when he compared it to giving a surveyor the task of measuring the parallax of points four miles away, by observations from a base-line two inches long! Small wonder that Tycho could find no stellar parallax even when using his nineteen-foot quadrant! He concluded that if the theory of Copernicus were true, the stars would be of incredible size. Ironically, Galileo's telescope showed just this. The planets became discs of light under magnification, but the stars remained points of light; hence they were enormously distant, and fantastically luminous. Unfor-

Fig. 2.10   In January, star *B* would seem to be on the right of star *A*; in July, it would seem to be on the left. The absence of this movement led Tycho and others to reject heliocentric hypotheses. The movement does take place, but needs extremely delicate instruments to detect it.

tunately, Tycho Brahe died in 1601, nine years before Galileo made this discovery, but the superb set of observations passed into the hands of the man who finally succeeded in describing the planetary courses accurately, though he could provide no satisfactory reason why they should go the way they did.

This man was Johann Kepler (1571–1630), a German of mathematical genius that amounted almost to mania. He was easily led astray by brilliant mathematical ideas, but he had the patience and skill in computation to sift their implications, and to reject them when false. Forward-looking in many ways (he was from his youth a convinced Copernican), he yet believed in astrology, and followed Pythagoras in looking for a celestial harmony that would be mathematically and aesthetically satisfying. He first became known in 1596, when he published a book, *Mysterium Cosmographicum*, propounding one of the most abstract and beautiful pictures of the universe that has ever been thought of.

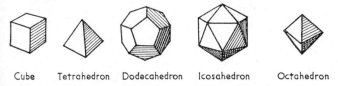

Cube   Tetrahedron   Dodecahedron   Icosahedron   Octahedron

Fig. 2.11 The five regular solids.

There are five, and only five, geometrically regular solid bodies: the cube, tetrahedron, dodecahedron, icosahedron and octahedron (see Fig. 2.11). These regular polyhedra, he believed, were arranged one inside the other to space out the orbits of the planets. The sun was in the middle, and the sphere of Mercury came next. Round the sphere of Mercury was circumscribed an octahedron. Circumscribing this octahedron was the sphere of Venus, itself inscribed in an icosahedron – and so on. The order therefore was: Saturn, *cube*, Jupiter, *tetrahedron*, Mars, *dodecahedron*, the Earth and Moon, *icosahedron*, Venus, *octahedron*, Mercury (see Fig. 2.12). Thus there could be only six planets, the five regular solids determining the space between their orbits. Kepler went to Tycho Brahe for the accurate figures of planetary motions, and inspired that nobleman with enthusiasm for his idea. Unfortunately, Tycho's data disproved the theory.

Kepler, undaunted, set to work to discover what really were the laws of planetary motion. Tycho gave him the data for the orbit of Mars, which was the hardest. Kepler worked out the orbit according to all the current theories,

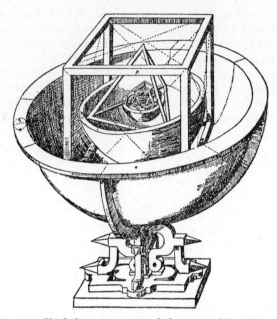

Fig. 2.12 Kepler's arrangements of planetary orbits within the spaces between the five regular solids.

including a modification of the Copernican theory, which he had thought of for himself. But the observed position of Mars differed by 8 or 9 minutes of arc from the best theoretical Copernican position. Kepler therefore took the unprecedented decision to drop uniform circular motion, which he said had robbed him of years of labour. No centre could be found for a circular orbit for Mars, which would explain the apparent changes in velocity of the planet's course. Eventually, he propounded orbits that were philosophical dynamite.

He enunciated three laws:

1. Planets move in ellipses with the sun at one focus.

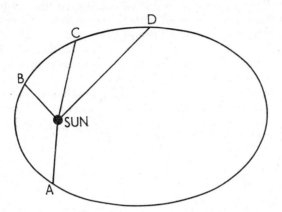

Fig. 2.13 Kepler's second law: The planet moves from *A* to *B*, from *B* to *C*, and from *C* to *D*, in equal times, if the areas *ASB*, *BSC* and *CSD* are equal.

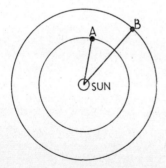

Fig. 2.14 Kepler's third law: If the period of planet *A* is x hours, and the period of planet *B* is y hours, then:

$$\frac{x^2}{y^2} = \frac{SA^3}{SB^3}$$

2. Each planet moves so that a line from the sun to the planet sweeps out equal areas in equal times (hence the planet moves faster when nearer to the sun – see Fig. 2.13).

3. The squares of the periods of revolution of all the planets are proportional to the cubes of their average distances from the sun (see Fig. 2.14).

Kepler's mathematics were unimpeachable, but there was much speculation about why planets *should* move like this. Kepler himself was not pleased. He referred to his elliptical orbits as 'a cartful of dung'.

THREE

The devilish cannon touches

The development of artillery, from small beginnings in the early fourteenth century, to the accurately bored cannon of the sixteenth, had a profound effect on mankind in many ways, most of them beneficial. The sheer power of artillery was unprecedented; man had never before possessed such concentrated might. Shakespeare was evidently among those impressed, and in his description of the siege of Harfleur, in *Henry V*, speaks of how

> . . . the nimble gunner
> With linstock now the devilish cannon touches
> And down goes all before them.

And to drive home the point a cannon was shot off backstage (which was, in the Elizabethan theatre, quite close to the audience). The cost of stage artillery was considerable; but the cost of siege artillery was enormous.

This had several important effects. One of the most obvious was that the status of the feudal lord was severely reduced. Before the introduction of effective artillery, any local magnate could defy the central authority from behind his castle walls for a long time, and a combination of barons could overturn the government. Thus the government had to be carried on with baronial consent. But as soon as the king possessed the means of blowing a hole in the baron's castle wall, the baron's opinions were far less important, and his influence on even local affairs withered. On the other hand, the cost of an artillery train was so huge that a natural alliance sprang up between the king who needed the guns and the merchants who could pay for them. The displacement of baronial by commercial influence at court naturally followed.

The cost of cannon led to a natural desire by rulers to make economies in their manufacture, transport and use. A profession of military engineers thus arose, using mathematical methods, conducting experiments, plotting the relationship between the course of the cannon-ball and the quantity of charge exploded, the elevation of the muzzle, and the weight of the projectile. The results of such experiments provided data of a kind unknown to Aristotle; such velocities were quite unheard of in antiquity. As a consequence, Aristotle's ideas on dynamics had already been much modified when the learned world was upset by the new astronomical facts. The process was slow, but the new laws of earthly motion were to prove as philosophically revolutionary as the new laws of heavenly motion, with which they were finally reconciled. Improved forms of gunpowder had been invented as early as the middle of the fifteenth century, but it was a hundred years before a gun-metal was devised capable of using it to full effect – hence the topical importance of ballistic measurements.

Aristotle had divided motion into two kinds, natural and violent. Natural motion was towards a 'natural place', such as the falling of a stone towards the centre of the earth, or the rising of a flame towards the sphere of fire. All other movement was of an unnatural, or violent character, and continued only as long as there was an impressed force. The velocity of a body in violent movement was proportional to that force. Living creatures alone were capable of self-determined movement. This belief was a very reasonable one in a country of rough roads and ox-carts, where motion, apart from falling motion, is imposed only with great difficulty, and only a few anomalies of movement needed to be explained.

One of these difficulties was the acceleration of falling bodies. Until it was possible to measure the speeds of a falling object, of course, physics had only to explain a *qualitative* increase in speed. What could be more obvious, then, that a stone speeded up so that it could as soon as possible attain its natural place in the universe? The acceleration of falling bodies was in ancient times, and indeed until fairly recently, the only example of acceleration that existed. Only falling bodies got faster – everything else slowed down.

The movement of projectiles also demanded a special explanation. Aristotle mentioned two possible theories why a stone or an arrow should keep on moving after it had left the hand or the bow. One explanation (Plato's) was that a projectile compressed the air in front of it, and this air circulated to the back, to fill up the vacuum that was impossible; this air then acted as a mover, whereupon a further layer of air was compressed in front, and acted in a similar way. Aristotle himself believed that the hand, or bow, imparted to the neighbouring air, the 'power of conveying motion'. When the projectile had been moved on by this air, there was still enough power left to pass on the 'power of conveying motion' to the next layer of air, and so on. These answers were couched in subtle philosophical language, which must have proved very satisfying to generation after generation of speculative metaphysicians; but it is difficult to believe that any artilleryman, or even archer, could have entertained either explanation for a moment.

It is important to note that the idea of 'action at a distance', exemplified for us daily by electrical, magnetic or gravitational attraction, was quite foreign to thinkers before the late seventeenth century. According to Aristotle, if something moved, it must be due to the action of the nature of the body itself, or something in contact with it. He was acquainted with magnetism and the attraction of light particles by rubbed amber (the word *electricity* derives from the Greek word for amber), but these phenomena were thought unimportant and did not inspire the idea of action at a distance, which is a very sophisticated concept, not easily accepted even by the men of the late seventeenth century.

Yet even in medieval times there had been critics of certain aspects of Aristotle's mechanics. Jean Buridan (*c.*1300–*c.*1358), a distinguished French scholastic, advanced a series of objections to the traditional theories of motion. In the first place, if a grindstone or a potter's wheel is set in motion, it will carry on moving for an appreciable time after the hand is released, and the heavier the wheel, the more persistent the motion. Clearly, the shape of a grindstone rules out any possibility that the air is pushing it round. On the contrary, the air, and the axle bearing, are slowing the grindstone down, and dissipating a stored-up force.

A stone thrown vertically upwards, Buridan considered, carries with it such a stored-up force, which he called *impetus*, which is gradually countered by air resistance and by its weight. As it falls, it begins to store up an *impetus* which moves it in combination with its weight – hence it accelerates.

This theory was conceived rather as a correction to Aristotle than as an overthrow of his philosophy, and Buridan used all the Aristotelian terms to state his case. However, the concept of *impetus* was a very fruitful one, which when given mathematical expression by Galileo, Descartes and Newton, was to lead to the modern idea of momentum.

Leonardo da Vinci (1452–1519) made considerable advances in mechanical science, although he failed to produce an all-embracing theory of motion. Typically, he was the man of practical experience. In 1483, when he offered his services to the Duke of Milan, he explained how his skill lay in civil and military engineering, particularly the latter, in the handling of explosives, military machinery, levers, pulleys, and so on. His theoretical work was also quite important, and included many of the principles now taught in the elementary physics class. He developed the theories of levers, pulleys, and the pressure of liquids. He recognized the impossibility of perpetual motion, and was aware of the principle of work. He measured the speed of falling objects, and found that they received a uniform acceleration, whether the fall were free or down a ramp. Leonardo was the engineer, rather than the scholar, although he was a mathematician of great skill. Throughout his life he accepted the theories of motion of Aristotle, but his solutions to practical problems were practical, and had much effect on his successors.

Simon Stevin (1548–1620), a Dutch engineer and mathematician, made further contributions to the study of motion. Like Leonardo, he applied mathematical methods to practical problems, disregarding Aristotle's qualitative ideas rather than trying to refute them. To him is due the well-known proposition in hydrostatics that the pressure of a liquid on the bottom of its container depends only on the depth, and is independent of the shape and size of the vessel. It was Stevin, too, who actually performed the experiment popularly attributed to Galileo, of dropping leaden weights, one ten times the size of the other, to test whether the heavier ball travelled faster. The balls were dropped from a height of thirty feet on to a plank, and only one sound of impact was heard. The result of this experiment was published in 1586, but such was the prestige of the Aristotelian philosophy that the learned world in general still believed that the speed of motion was proportional to the impressed force, and that therefore, a weight ten times the size of another would fall ten times as fast.

The contribution of Galileo, in dynamics as in astronomy, was fundamental. In the first place, he was very clear on the distinction between words and things, which was, and still is, a prime cause of muddled thinking. He criticized the proposition that bodies fall because of gravity, not because it was wrong, but because it said nothing. Gravity merely means 'the quality of being heavy', that is, indeed, the quality of falling when released. Galileo saw, moreover, that discussion about the cause of the acceleration of falling bodies should be deferred until the manner in which bodies actually fell, and accelerated in so doing, was investigated and measured. The task of science was not to look for the ultimate natures or purposes of things, but to describe the immediate chain of cause and effect.

Galileo had a great influence on experimental method. His starting-point was practical experience – sheer observation of how workmen lifted heavy weights, or how shipbuilders found it necessary to prop up heavy vessels before launching, but not lighter ones. At the very beginning of his book *Dialogues concerning Two New Sciences*, which deals with the strength of materials, and with motion, we find this interest in practical achievement as a spur to speculation.

Salviati : The constant activity which you Venetians display in your famous arsenal suggests to the studious mind a large field for investigation, especially that part of the work which involves mechanics; for in this department all types of instruments and machines are constantly being constructed by many artisans, among whom there must be some who, partly by inherited experience and partly by their own observations, have become highly expert and clever in explanation.

Sagredo : You are quite right. Indeed, I myself, being curious by nature, frequently visit this place for the mere pleasure of observing the work of those who, on account of their superiority over other artisans, we call 'first-rank men'. Conference with them has often helped me in the investigation of certain effects, including not only those which are striking, but also those which are recondite and almost incredible. At times also I have been put to confusion and driven to despair of ever explaining something for which I could not account, but which my senses told me to be true.

The practical world, then, suggests lines of research and provides some of the answers.

But at this stage, Galileo emphasizes the need for mathematics. The mathematical treatment needs to be applied to one's suppositions about the causes of phenomena, so that predictions may be made, which can be practically tested. Galileo believed that it was geometry, rather than logic, which would stimulate the discovery of scientific laws, while logic was of service in testing them. Galileo's success in this method depended very largely on his skill in isolating the factors that ought to be mathematically treated, and then measured, and excluding the irrelevant ones.

In the investigation of the motion of falling bodies, Galileo realized at an early stage that the reason why some bodies fell more quickly than others was that air resistance acted unequally on them during the fall. To prove that different bodies fell at equal speeds, but for the resistance of the air, it was necessary to use the slowest speeds possible. For at slow speeds, measurement would be easier, and the air resistance would be less. He needed some device for magnifying any small differences between the times of fall of different bodies, to make them more easily observable. These conditions Galileo found in the pendulum. If unequal bodies fell with different speeds, then the times of oscillation of pendulums of equal length, but with bobs made of cork and lead, would be unequal; they would, if lined up and started together, gradually get out of phase. If unequal bodies fell with equal speeds, the two pendulums should keep in phase; even though the cork bob would slow down

much more quickly than the lead one, they would keep
swinging in time with one another. Experiment showed that
such pendulums did swing together. This result, obtainable
indoors, was more convincing in its simplicity than the
spectacular dropping of cannon-balls from the Leaning
Tower would have been.

It is true that Galileo did not always make the experiments which his mathematics, and his inventive genius,
suggested. Often the use of 'thought-experiments' rather
than actual experiments was of no great matter, since his
appeal was to an obvious extension of common experience.
But common experience was not always reliable. One
experiment in dynamics, which had considerable bearing
on the astronomical dispute, was about what would happen
if a stone were dropped from the mast of a ship, first at
anchor, second when in full sail. The Aristotelians maintained that the stone would fall farther back in the second
case than in the first. Galileo maintained that it would not.
In fact, the experiment was not actually tried out until
1641, when it was found, of course, that, provided the ship
was in steady motion, it made no difference to the place
where the stone fell. But if Galileo often used 'thought-
experiments', other people used many more, sometimes to
the exclusion of actual experiments, and at least in theory,
Galileo was an experimentalist. As he says himself, 'One
single experiment or conclusive proof to the contrary would
be enough to batter to the ground a great many probable
arguments'.

Galileo wittily exemplified his principle of the separate
testing of variables when commenting on an ancient writer
who maintained that the Babylonians used to cook eggs
through friction against the air, by whirling them in a sling.
Today, said Galileo, we cannot so cook eggs, even though
we have the same eggs, and slings, and stout fellows to
whirl them. The cause of the different effect must therefore
lie in the one point of difference – that we are not Baby-

Ionians! In his pendulum experiments he separately tested
the important variable factors: the arc of swing, the weight
of the bob, the length of the line, and the period of oscillation. In that way he found that the period of oscillation
was proportional to the square root of the length of line,
and was independent of the weight of the bob and of the
length of the arc of swing. Having given his conclusions,
he is quick to point out applications of his laws – that the
length of any pendulum can be found merely by timing its
swing.

Two other important contributions which Galileo made
to the understanding of motion were his studies of balls
running down slopes and his treatment of projectile motion.
The measurement of the times of descent of balls rolling
down inclined planes was productive of very fruitful results.
Such accelerated motion is slower – the whole process of fall
is diluted, and much more easily measured by the water-
clock than is vertical fall. (The accurate pendulum clock
was only invented much later.) From these studies, he was
able to give a mathematical form to what Buridan had
called *impetus,* and which he called *momentum.*

Persistence of motion, he said, was not dependent on a
constant impressed force. It was *change* of motion, an
increase or decrease in velocity or a change of direction,
which required an impressed force. This concept explained
theoretically the path of a cannon-ball, since if air-resistance
were neglected its horizontal velocity would be maintained
for ever, were it not that the ball is subject to a constant
acceleration downwards, because of its weight. The resultant
of these two motions is a parabola. This could be confirmed
by the simple calculation that the range of a cannon, on this
line of argument, ought to be at its maximum at an angle
of elevation of 45 degrees, and that the range of a cannon
elevated at 35 degrees ought to be the same as at 55 degrees,
and so on – predictions found to be true (see Fig. 3.1.).

Galileo did not quite formulate Newton's first law of

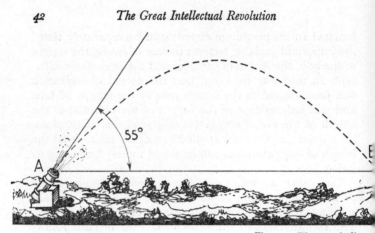

Fig. 3.1 The parabolic c〈

motion, that if no force is impressed on a body, it will either remain at rest, or move in a straight line at a constant velocity, though his work certainly inspired the law. Galileo wished to generalize his dynamics to include the heavenly bodies, which he believed had a circular motion by nature. He therefore concluded that terrestrial bodies conserved by nature a circular motion, like the heavenly bodies, straight-line motion being simply our observation of tiny segments of circular motion of large radius. With everything moving naturally in circles, he did not arrive at the idea of 'action at a distance', which was philosophically distasteful – even with the example of magnetic forces, which Galileo had studied, to lead the way. What prevented Galileo from anticipating Newton's work of drawing together the heavens and the earth into one dynamical system, was that he had not seen the truth of Kepler's discoveries,* and that his large circles were still not quite straight lines.

The opposition that Galileo's views met from the Church had several causes. Aristotle's philosophy had, more or less

* Perhaps because he had not had the patience to make his way through Kepler's very prolix and rambling books.

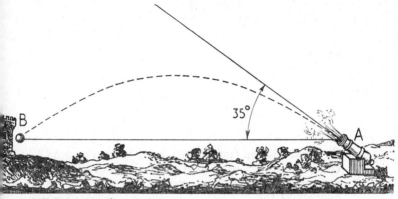

35°

nnon-ball demonstrated.

accidentally, become accepted among churchmen. After the turmoil of the Reformation, the Church needed a period of peace, of freedom from controversy; and Galileo's ideas on the movement of the earth upset that peace. Moreover, his views, based partly on facts more immediately significant to master builders and shipwrights than to cloistered ecclesiastics, were published in the vernacular Italian instead of the learned Latin. The Church authorities were quite willing for the theory that the earth moved round the sun to be discussed in learned circles as a hypothesis, but did not want the idea proclaimed as a fact to the general public. Galileo always maintained that he was a faithful son of the Church; but his ideas of momentum were gradually building up a mechanical world-picture, which others might accept without the Mechanic. Galileo's opponents wanted time to work out the theological changes needed, before his theory went before the public. Cannon were changing the world. For cannon meant high velocities, and high velocities meant more mathematics to calculate them.

FOUR

All coherence gone

Sir Francis Bacon (1561–1626), King James I's Lord Chancellor from 1617 until 1621 (when he was disgraced for accepting bribes), is always pointed out as one of the forerunners of the intellectual revolution of the seventeenth century. Ironically enough, he did not make a single scientific discovery himself, and often failed to give due credit to those who had made them. Thus he writes slightingly of 'the opinion of Copernicus touching the rotation of the earth which astronomy itself cannot correct, because it is not repugnant to any of the phenomena, yet natural philosophy may correct'. Most of the ideas he propounded about scientific method had been said before, and some of them are unsound. Yet he did much to publicize a new way of looking at learning as a means whereby mankind might gain mastery over the forces of nature. Freed from the scholastic association with metaphysics and religion and instead aligned with the experience gained from useful crafts, such learning, Bacon expected, would lead to discoveries and inventions through which the mastery might be achieved.

Bacon's principal works were *The Advancement of Learning*, published in 1605, *Novum Organum*, published 1620, and *The New Atlantis*, published posthumously in 1627. The first two works deal with the directions Bacon thought learning might profitably take; the last outlines a utopian state, one of the interesting features of which is a college, the 'House of Solomon', devoted to the useful arts and sciences. Just such a college, though on a limited scale, had been founded in 1598 under the will of Sir Thomas Gresham (1518–79), which endowed the establishment and put control in the hands of a group of merchants. There were professors in Divinity, Civil Law, Rhetoric, Music, Physic, Geometry and Astronomy, who lectured free, in Latin and English.

There was a great need for such an establishment at that time. No scientist could secure any relevant education at Oxford and Cambridge, where it was impossible to learn such subjects as geometry or astronomy through official channels. The two old universities were in a period of decline: they were producing time-serving parsons and amusing the sons of the gentry. Gresham College, on the other hand, in the heart of London, was linked to the needs of navigation, trade, surveying, manufactures, the Royal Navy and the East India Company. It was through the activities typical of Gresham College that Bacon saw the possibilities of bettering man's lot. It was no accident that the class of merchants, manufacturers, ships' captains, tradesmen in the broadest sense, were nearly all of Puritan sympathies; they were impatient of restrictions on free speech, even more impatient of restrictions on trade, such as monopolies, and moreover, were people to whom mathematics were a familiar tool.

Bacon was the mouthpiece of the new, self-made men, who were intruding themselves into political life and were eventually to form the parliamentary party in the Civil War. The newly rich in all ages have tried to use their wealth to buy themselves positions of prestige and power. The new class of merchants, manufacturers, and financiers, operating in London and such other important and growing towns as Bristol, Norwich, Boston and Hull, tended to buy country estates or marry heiresses of them and gain seats in the House of Commons, where they were generally in alliance with the established country gentry. This alliance was only to break down on the very eve of Civil War, when the old landowning members, pushed to the limit, tended to react feudally, while the 'new men' generally supported those constitutional checks and privileges which favoured them.

For the medieval Schoolmen, those upholders of the philosophical systems deriving ultimately from Aristotle, Bacon had the utmost scorn. There was, he said, too much logical superstructure working up from too little solid fact. The Schoolmen, he said,

having sharp and strong wits, and abundance of leisure, and small variety of reading, but their wits being shut up in the cells of a few authors (chiefly Aristotle their dictator) as their persons were shut up in the cells of monasteries and colleges, and knowing little history, either of nature or time, did out of no great quantity of matter, and infinite agitation of wit spin out unto those laborious webs of learning which are extant in their books. For the wit and mind of man, if it work upon matter, which is the contemplation of the creatures of God, worketh according to the stuff, and is limited thereby; but if it work upon itself, as the spider worketh his web, then it is endless, and brings forth indeed cobwebs of learning, admirable for the fineness of thread and work, but of no substance or profit.

(The Advancement of Learning)

Bacon further recommended the rigorous sifting of evidence, instancing the evils which arose through the too eager admission of reports of miracles, in ecclesiastical history. Those who disbelieved the stories when they first arose had allowed them to pass, regarding them as a species of pious poesy, while the public believed them through ignorance.

Yet after a period of time, when the mist began to clear up, they grew to be esteemed but as old wives' fables,

impostures of the clergy, illusions of spirits, and badges of
Antichrist, to the great scandal and detriment of religion.
(*The Advancement of Learning*)

The Puritan party was, in religious affairs, thinking
strongly along these lines. The abuses in the Roman Church
were intimately associated with the claim of Pope and
priesthood to interpret religion. The Puritan merchants
and craftsmen, who had acquired a practical education in
the pursuit of business, felt the intervention of the ecclesiastic
to be hampering, rather than helpful, in the interpretation
of the Bible. Moreover, a close business connection existed
between London and the Calvinist Netherlands, where, if
anything, commercial enterprise and daring speculation
were even more admired than in England. Science and
business were anticlerical. Even when, as in 1644, the
Presbyterian cause seemed triumphant, such Puritan
thinkers as Milton warned of the danger that 'new Presbyter
is but old Priest writ large', and that speculation should be
free from any kind of clerical censorship. Milton's tract in
favour of free speech, *Areopagitica*, said that if the ministers
were allowed the powers of the expelled bishops, they would
become like them.

For while Bacon was pointing the way to scientific
advance, the purpose of which he enunciated as 'for the
glory of the Creator and the relief of man's estate', the
clerical establishment was clamping down firmer controls on
the expression of opinion. James I had seen very clearly that
his interest lay in alliance with the authoritarian episcopacy:
'No Bishop, no King', as he had put it. Religion, politics,
and the new philosophy were found to be much bound
together. Newspapers were forbidden, and the news letters,
by which the great gathered home and foreign information,
were extremely expensive and had a very limited effect.
The press was censored by the bishops, working through the
Court of Star Chamber, and savage penalties awaited the

illegal printer who was caught. Under Charles I the bishops had infiltrated heavily into high civil office, and under Archbishop Laud the censorship was at its height.

In these circumstances control of the pulpit assumed importance. The upper churchmen knew that science was as much an enemy as Calvinism. In 1618, Archdeacon Barlow, well connected with the episcopacy, regretted that 'mechanics' preferred experiment to Scripture. Of the earth's rotation he remarked that although arguments in its favour might pass in a mechanical tradesman's shop, they were very insufficient to be allowed for good by learned men and Christians by profession. His episcopal relations had the power to see to it that Copernican, Presbyterian or even mildly reformist doctrines were never preached from a pulpit.

The Crown and the Church (in the 1630s Laud in one capacity or another) controlled university appointments. The bishop of every diocese had the right to license teachers, and to forbid ministers to preach – in fact, sixty per cent of ministers were non-preaching. An attempt by a group of wealthy Puritan merchants and lawyers to buy up the rights of presentation of ministers to certain parishes, especially parishes where M.P.s lived, was recognized as a back-door political manœuvre, and suppressed. As Milton pointed out in *Areopagitica*, in a reference to his Italian tour of 1639 (when he visited Galileo, then old and under house arrest for his opinions), while Italians might envy the comparative freedom of expression in England, real freedom was still to come (freedom of the press had to wait until 1694). Among the many and complicated causes leading to the Civil War, the muzzling of opinion was certainly important.

A recent historian called Bacon 'the Turgot of the English Revolution' – the one man who might have averted it. Unfortunately, he was removed from office by a shabby political conspiracy, and was unable to prevent the catastrophe which even in 1620 the long-sighted could foresee. His political skill might have reconciled the Puritans to government and the Stuart kings to progress.

He is the great advocate of the inductive method. He proposed, for instance, that in the study of heat the first step was to draw up lists of instances and opposites. Such a list would include on the one hand the heat of the sun, fire, hot springs, pepper, and the slaking of quicklime; and on the other hand the rays of the moon, water, cold winds, the air in cellars, and so on. From these lists, says Bacon, it should be possible to determine the essential nature, or what he called the 'form' of heat, through careful examination of what is present in the former list and negatived in the latter. This is the opposite method from the scholastic one of starting from a number of dogmas, and working out their consequences. As a methodologist, Bacon had two shortcomings. He under-valued the use of hypothesis in science – the really creative part. He thought that by correct use of his inductive method, anyone could become a scientist. Experience shows that the great scientist is he who can imagine a hypothesis to explain the phenomena being investigated, and can so work out its consequences that a crucial experiment is possible, one which will establish a whole chain of reasoning.

Bacon also underestimated the use of mathematics, which he refers to in *The Advancement of Learning* as though it were no more than a mental gymnasium (Napier was inventing logarithms in the early years of the century, and great advances were being made in geometry, algebra, trigonometry, and other studies – for use in navigation, surveying, and the mechanical arts). Yet as a politician, he was able to advocate to James I that official support should be given to the new sciences. James, however, was a pedant in the true scholastic tradition, and refused. The chance of some political coherence between the old and new philosophies was lost.

Even though government support may not have been forthcoming, England was an exciting place for a scientist to live in during the early seventeenth century. In 1600, William Gilbert (1546–1603), Queen Elizabeth's physician, published an important book, *De Magnete*, dealing in detail with the properties of magnets and the nature of the earth's magnetism. In 1628, William Harvey (1578–1657), an English doctor who had studied at Cambridge and Padua (the latter at the time when Galileo was holding a professorship there), and later had become Sir Francis Bacon's medical adviser, announced his discovery of the circulation of the blood. Galen, the great ancient medical authority whose works were still at this time the standard text, had regarded the arteries and veins as forming separate systems. Harvey was able to infer, though not to prove, the existence of capillaries through which the blood passes from artery to vein (see Plate 4); they were seen for the first time in 1661, by an Italian named Malpighi, using an improved form of compound microscope. Harvey never understood the function of respiration, because, as is well known, the composition of the air and the nature of oxidation were not understood until the work of Lavoisier, who died in the French Revolution; but Harvey's discovery cleared up a major error in medical science, and provided a further example of the fallibility of ancient authorities.

Napier's invention of logarithms was published in 1614, and seven years later Edmund Gunter invented the slide rule, which works on a logarithmic principle. Astronomical research was being carried on by Thomas Hariot, a member of Sir Walter Ralegh's circle. Hariot corresponded with Kepler, and like the latter was a fine mathematician. Sir Walter Ralegh himself, during his imprisonment by James I in the Tower, carried out scientific experiments, and had a detailed knowledge of current research, particularly as it affected navigation.

The colonization of North America played its part in

bringing about the new outlook. Ralegh's name is, of course, associated with the first, unsuccessful attempt to colonize Virginia; and his policies were continued from 1612 onwards, largely by Puritan interests. (Neither James I nor Charles I had much sympathy for these ventures. Britain's strength on the sea between 1603 and 1642 was that of her merchants, not that of her navy. In the middle of this period, Algerian corsairs were regularly operating round Britain, and even taking prisoners in the Faroe Islands and Iceland.) The discovery and exploration of new land brought new facts (in geography and botany, for example) for the thinker to speculate on.

Hakluyt's *Voyages of the English Nation*, published in 1600, gives a vivid account of this pushing, industrious, bold, speculative maritime world, as it existed on the eve of the century. It seems to illustrate the temper of the times that a country vicar should collect and publish commercial papers, while King James was engaged on *A Counterblast to Tobacco* – that new American herb everyone was beginning to take. As Shakespeare's times gave way to Milton's, and as the flood of precious metals from America brought about a steady inflation, the tensions grew. It would be foolish to attribute the English Civil War entirely, or even largely, to intellectual currents. But for men to revolt against an established form of government, abolish lords, abolish bishops, and bring a king to trial and cut off his head in the name of the people (instead of sending a ruffian to murder him in prison), shows that more than a mere struggle for power was in operation. Men were prepared to think adventurously, even in political matters.

FIVE

The admirable Descartes

It was in England that the scientific and intellectual revolution was proceeding fastest, and in England, too, that the political tensions of forty years added drama to the intellectual differences of the traditionalists and the moderns. In 1614 a Scottish writer, well acquainted with the English scene, commented on the widespread opposition to the Aristotelian world-picture and the support for Copernican astronomy. 'In philosophy and the mathematics, in geography and astronomy, there is no opinion so prodigious and strange but in that island was either invented or hath found followers and subtile instancers,' he wrote. The same might well have been said about Holland, which, intellectually, was at this period the freest country in Europe. Books which could not even have been submitted to the censors in other countries poured regularly from the presses of Amsterdam.

Germany, where the work of Tycho Brahe and Kepler had been carried out, ran into the misfortune of the Thirty Years War (1619–48), when armies of various nationalities, on what was originally a religious quarrel, fought, plundered and destroyed town and country. The population was reduced to a quarter of what it had been,* and the entire basis of intellectual life was stamped out for a hundred years.

* This figure has of late been disputed, probably with some justification. But at the very least, the effects of the war on the German population were harrowing in the extreme.

Plate 1 Medieval learning symbolically represented in a print of 1508. Literacy (symbolized by the figure giving a horn-book to a new pupil) unlocks the way to a hierarchy of different studies. At the very top stands Peter Lombard, representing Theology or Metaphysics. Other figures represent such medieval authorities as Seneca, Euclid, Ptolemy and Aristotle, governing the lesser studies.

Plate 2 A representation of the medieval world-picture. In the very centre lies the earth, surrounded by clouds, and a number of comets, one in the shape of a sword. The sphere of fire follows, completing the tally of the elements. The Moon, Mercury, Venus, the Sun, Mars, Jupiter and Saturn are represented by appropriate figures standing on wheels upon their several spheres, while the spheres themselves are given their traditional astrological signs, such as ♀ for Venus. The sphere of the Fixed Stars is shown in black, and is studded with the symbols for the signs of the Zodiac. Outside this is the Crystal Sphere; and then the Primum Mobile, full of wheels to symbolize its function of conveying motion to the planetary spheres. Outside everything is the Empyrean Heaven, the dwelling-place of God and the Saints.

HIMMEL·DES·LICHTS·WOHNVNG·GOTTES·VND·ALLER·AVSERWEHLTEN·

um mobile

Kristall Sphære

Sphære der Fixsterne

Sphære des Mondes

Sphære des Merkur

Sphære der Venus

Sphære der Sonne

Sphære des Mars

Sphære des Jupiter

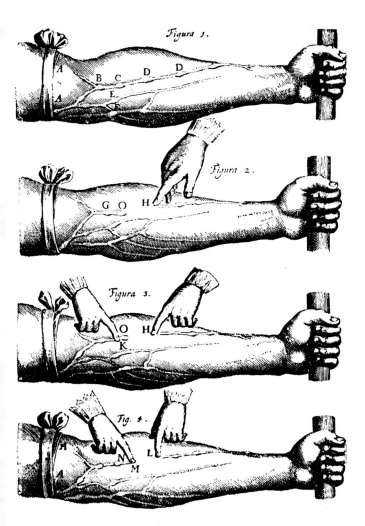

Plate 4 Some of Harvey's experiments showing the action of valves in the veins.

Plate 3 (opposite) Astronomy in 1651. Urania, the Muse of Astronomy, is comparing the different systems. Ptolemy's earth-centred system lies discarded at her feet. She is judging between that of Copernicus, left, and of Tycho Brahe, on the right, and giving greater weight to the latter. In her left hand is an astrolabe. The hand at the top of the picture extends three fingers marked Number, Measure and Weight – the criteria of the new science.

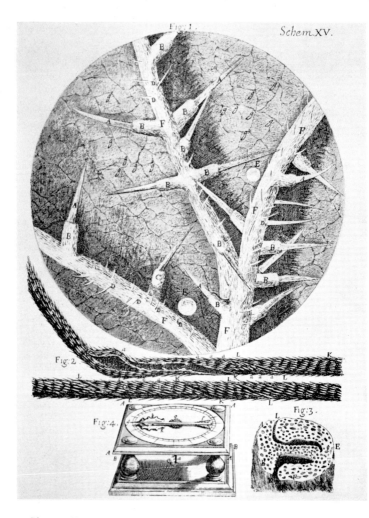

Plate 5 From Robert Hooke's *Micrographia*, published 1665. Fig. 1 shows the underside of the leaf of a stinging nettle. Figs. 2 and 3 show the beard of wild oats, in wet and dry conditions, and Fig. 4 his ingenious hygrometer, for measuring the humidity of the atmosphere, using the rolling and unrolling of the beard under different weather conditions, to move a pointer across a scale.

Plate 6 (opposite) Hooke's aerial telescope. It was not possible in the seventeenth century to construct a tube adequate for the mounting of an object-lens of very long focal length.

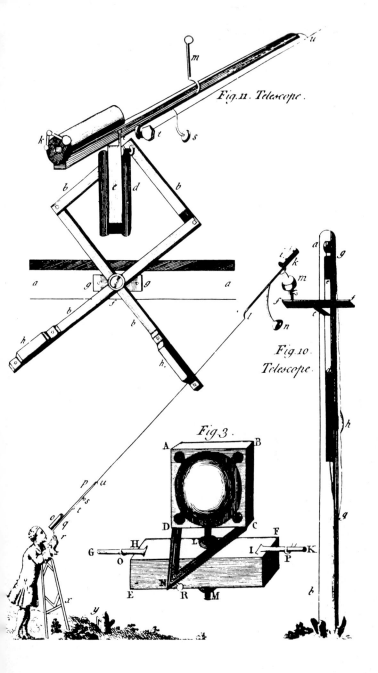

Fig. 11. Telescope.

Fig. 10.
Telescope.

Fig. 3.

Plate 7 A replica of Newton's original reflecting telescope, showing the cup-and-ball joint on which it is mounted, and the screw by which it is focused.

In Italy the discouragement accorded to Galileo dampened scientific fervour considerably (though Galileo's pupil Torricelli was to prove an important figure, as were several others). In Spain there had been no learning worth the name since the expulsion of the Moors and Jews in the early sixteenth century, and the establishment of the notorious Spanish Inquisition, which strangled or burned anyone who differed from rigid Catholic belief (and continued doing so as late as 1835). France was luckier. France was Roman Catholic in religion, but normally allied with the Protestant powers politically. Besides, there was in France a tradition of fairly free intellectual speculation, provided that a nominal acceptance of the Church's authority was made now and again, and provided the ideas were confined to learned circles. And so France was able to nourish René Descartes (1596–1650).

Descartes was born at la Haye in Touraine, of a wealthy and noble family. His mental prowess was recognized at a very early age, and at ten he was sent by his wise father to the Jesuit *Collège de la Flèche*, then recently founded and reckoned to provide the best education in the country. He studied the humanities, philosophy, and mathematics. Already, by the age of sixteen, he was intensely aware of the uncertainty and unsatisfactory nature of what philosophers had taught (especially Aristotle), compared with the wonderful certainty and precision of mathematics. As he later wrote:

I was especially delighted with the Mathematics, on account of the certitude and evidence of their reasonings: but I had not as yet a precise knowledge of their true use; and thinking that they but contributed to the advancement of the mechanical arts, I was astonished that foundations, so strong and solid, should have had no loftier superstructure reared on them.

The University of Poitiers confirmed his belief that only

E

in mathematics was there any certainty, and that no other branch of learning was more than the building of words on words. For a few months he lived a gay life in Paris, until he became bored with its shallowness. Then, as he tells us:

I spent the remainder of my youth in travelling, in visiting courts and armies, in holding intercourse with men of different dispositions and ranks, in collecting varied experience, in proving myself in the different situations into which fortune threw me, and, above all, in making such reflection on the matter of my experience as to secure my improvement. For it occurred to me that I should find much more truth in the reasonings of each individual with reference to the affairs in which he is personally interested, and the issue of which must punish him if he has judged amiss, than in those conducted by a man of letters in his study, regarding speculative matters that are of no practical moment, and followed by no consequences to himself, further, perhaps, than that they foster his vanity the better the more remote they are from common sense; requiring, as they must in this case, the exercise of greater ingenuity and art to render them probable.

At the age of twenty-one, he decided to study the art of warfare under Prince Maurice of Nassau, incidentally gaining a considerable mathematical reputation in Holland. In 1619 he joined the Bavarian army which was setting out to conquer the territories of the Elector Palatine, whose assumption of the Bohemian crown had started the war in Germany. On 10 November, while he was in winter quarters at Ulm, he experienced a sudden enlightenment, analogous to a religious experience, though on the intellectual instead of the mystical level. As a consequence, he decided to pull down his entire philosophical structure and start again.

He resolved first to doubt. He would doubt every fact, every theory, that was in the smallest degree removed from certainty, and reject it, in order to be left with only such facts as could be certain. He rejected the learning of the schools, as being utterly uncertain. He rejected the evidence of his senses, since it is well known that the senses are often deceived, and could conceivably always be so. On the assumption that his senses were being manipulated by a wicked, powerful and ingenious demon, it was even possible to doubt the existence of his own body, and of the apparent certainties of mathematics. Only one thing it was impossible to doubt – his own existence, for if he did not exist, there could be nothing to do the doubting. 'I think, therefore I am,' he said. *Cogito ergo sum.*

Having established this principle as the bedrock on which to build his philosophical system, he proceeded to demonstrate, to his satisfaction, if not that of his readers, the existence of God. He doubted, and it was less perfect to doubt than to know. But whence arises this notion of perfection? The more perfect could not arise from the less perfect, so that a being infinite, eternal, immutable, omniscient and omnipotent, must exist. It was now possible for Descartes to build up the world again. A good God would not act like the deceitful demon he had imagined – so that whatever he could *clearly and distinctly* perceive was true. However, it was not easy, he admitted, to say what, in fact, could be perceived clearly and distinctly. We clearly see the sun, but it is much bigger than it looks.

Among the more clearly and distinctly perceived facts of the universe were naturally the truths of mathematics;* mathematics were, in fact, the only reality in nature. The universe was infinite in extent; matter and space were the same thing (and thus a vacuum was an impossibility); and matter was infinitely divisible. The world, Descartes maintained, was a huge machine. The quantity of movement in the world was constant. Animals were automata, quite incapable of voluntary action, but men had free-will.

* Descartes made original contributions to mathematics, especially in co-ordinate geometry.

The soul acted on the body through the pineal gland (a portion of the brain whose function is still obscure) where it came into contact with those Galenic entities, the 'vital spirits'. The soul could not affect the total quantity of movement in the universe, but it could affect the *direction* of movement of the 'vital spirits', and hence the workings of different parts of the body. Thus the worlds of mind and matter were independent but interacting – a system often known as dualism.

The motion of the planets was explained by a system of vortices, or whirlpools of subtle matter in which the planets were carried. With an eye on possible theological condemnation, however, he put forward this part of his theory as a hypothesis only. (This was one of the standard ways of avoiding a charge of heresy. The other was to go and live in Holland, which Descartes also did; but Descartes' Catholicism seems to have been sincere.) The entire Cartesian philosophy, especially its initial doubt, was a remarkable achievement. It included the love of God as well as the principle of inertia. It has stimulated thinkers ever since; and although it was open to criticisms in detail as soon as it was enunciated, and the vortex system was overthrown by Isaac Newton, the contemporaries of Descartes were in no doubt of his greatness, and referred to him in such terms as 'the admirable des-Cartes', a tribute alike to his genius and his charm.

The earliest of the many objections to Cartesianism was that motion was not only conserved in quantity, but also in direction. Therefore, the immaterial soul could not steer the material vital spirits by its free-will. Some of Descartes' followers tried to amend the philosophy by what is often called the 'two clocks' theory. This states that physical phenomena and mental phenomena *seem* to interact, just as a clock one can see may *seem* to be causing the chimes in a clock which one can only hear. But this theory demands such a constant interference by God to preserve the appearances that it has never found much favour. Joseph Glanvill, the author of a half-forgotten book called *The Vanity of Dogmatizing*, published in London in 1661, thought the problem insoluble:

It is the saying of the divine Plato, that man is nature's horizon; dividing betwixt the upper hemisphere of immaterial intellects, and this lower of corporeity: and that we are a compound of beings distant in extremes, is as clear as noon. But how the purer Spirit is united to this clod, is a knot too hard for fallen humanity to untie. What cement should unite heaven and earth, light and darkness, natures of so diverse a make, of such disagreeing attributes, which have almost nothing, but Being, in common; this is a riddle, which must be left to the coming of Elias. How should a thought be united to a marble statue, or a sunbeam to a lump of clay!

And even an amendment to the Cartesian theory, suggested by Dr. Henry More, said Glanvill, does not help.

Nor yet doth the ingenious hypothesis of the most excellent Cantabrigian philosopher, of the soul's being an *extended penetrable substance* relieve us; since, how that which *penetrates* all bodies without the least jog or obstruction, should impress a motion on any, is by his own confession alike inconceivable.

Cartesians, in fact, were faced with the problem of explaining to the world how to hit a cricket ball with a wreath of mist instead of a bat.

Besides the 'two clocks' theory (known as occasionalism*), two solutions were possible to the dualist difficulty. One was idealism: that mental events cause what we observe as material events, and that the pattern we observe in nature is really something inside our minds. The other solution is that of Thomas Hobbes, which will be described later: that mental events are simply due to matter in motion, and have

* Later as psycho-physical parallelism.

no independent existence. This is called materialism.* It is worth noting that this problem arises directly out of the discovery of the Principle of Inertia.

That Descartes should have maintained the impossibility of the vacuum was unfortunate, coming when it did. Galileo had already performed elementary experiments on the vacuum, by drawing an air-tight piston out of a closed

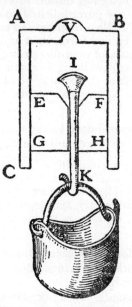

Fig. 5.1 Galileo's apparatus to demonstrate the existence of the vacuum. The cylinder was of metal or glass, and the plug of wood.

* Not, of course, the same use of the word as is found in newspaper editorials, sermons, political speeches, and pious talk, where it denotes that the holder of the belief prefers roast chicken, new curtains, television, and foreign holidays to newspaper editorials, sermons, political speeches and pious talk.

cylinder (see Fig. 5.1). He recorded the fact that pumps would not lift water higher than thirty-two feet, and assumed that the ancient maxim that 'nature abhors a vacuum' held true only to a limited extent.

In 1643, at the suggestion of Evangelista Torricelli (1608–47), a pupil of Galileo, a tube three feet long was filled to the brim with mercury, and inverted into a bath of the same fluid. The mercury in the tube fell to a height of about thirty inches, leaving a vacuum above. The fact that there was nothing in the space was proved by tilting the tube, when the mercury rose to the top – filling up all the space. Mercury is over thirteen times as dense as water, and Torricelli's experiment was easily repeated all over Europe, and wondered at. Nobody had seen nothing before.

The Aristotelians claimed that a tiny amount of air had, in fact, been left in the Torricellian vacuum, and was being pulled, like a spring, by the weight of the column of mercury. Descartes suggested that by an involved series of displacements, some of the 'subtle matter' from outside the atmosphere had insinuated itself into the space through the glass. Others claimed that the space was filled with vapours from the mercury (which happens to be true, though the quantity of mercury vapour is minute). Nobody found it easy to explain why the mercury level stopped where it did.

Blaise Pascal (1623–62), the French mathematician and physicist, made variations on Torricelli's experiment to clear matters up. In answer to the air-spring theory, Pascal performed the experiment with tubes of different lengths and shapes, and showed that the volume above the mercury could be varied easily, but that the height of the mercury was constant. The vapour pressure theory was refuted by a wonderful public experiment with tubes forty-six feet long. One of these was filled with water, another with red wine. The five hundred spectators were asked to predict which liquid column would be higher. The general opinion was that the wine would generate more vapour, so that the water column would be higher. Pascal already realized that the density of the fluid was the determining factor, and in fact, the wine column was found to be higher, when the tubes were inverted. (They were attached to ships' masts.)

Complete certainty of the true explanation of the Torricellian vacuum – that the mercury column was being balanced by the pressure of the air – was obtained by two further experiments. First, Pascal managed to prepare a barometer inside a barometer, when the two levels were found to be the same. Then, on 19 September 1648, Pascal's brother-in-law very carefully carried a mercury barometer up the Puy de Dôme, when the mercury column sank considerably. Obviously, nature had no horror of a vacuum, limited or otherwise. Air pressed down on the mercury; and at the top of a mountain, less air was pressing.

So the philosophy of Descartes had but a short time as a living system. But its *type* of world-picture – the mechanical model – has for three hundred years been a fruitful scientific idea.

SIX

That great leviathan

The fruitful ideas in any revolutionary scientific discovery tend to be applied, or misapplied, in other sciences, in religion and philosophy, and especially in politics. Darwin's discovery of the processes of biological evolution through natural selection and the survival of the fittest, for instance, has in our own time helped to inspire both the Communists and the National Socialists. The Communist is happy to draw his analogy between the struggle for survival among species and the struggle for political power between what he calls classes. The Nazi accepts the common misinterpretation of 'survival of the fittest' as survival of the most athletic (instead of the survival of the best adapted to the conditions, which may in some circumstances mean the least athletic), and draws support for his ideas on the superiority of what he calls his race, and its bounden duty to boss about the others. (Naturally, Darwin's ideas would have passed unnoticed among such people on their purely scientific merits.)

The really fruitful ideas in early seventeenth-century science were the concept of inertia, and the application of mathematical methods to scientific problems. These were seized upon by Thomas Hobbes (1588–1679) to build up a philosophy of materialism which had particular application to the political conditions of his day. Hobbes was far from being either a Nazi or a Communist, and would certainly have been horrified by the beliefs of either. On the other hand, his critics, in his lifetime and since, have variously, and unjustly, accused him of atheism, heresy, supporting the absolutism of Charles I, and toadying to Oliver Cromwell. Actually, he was a kindly, somewhat timid man, but a very incisive thinker who stood his philosophical ground. He was very anxious to use his intellectual gifts to avert the civil disorders of his times, by applying what seemed to him the certainties of geometrical method to the uncertainties of political science.

This was rather a new way of looking at politics. Admittedly, he had a predecessor in Nicolò Machiavelli (1469–1527), whose little book *The Prince*, written in 1513, treated of statecraft from a highly practical viewpoint, even to the inclusion of a section giving advice to those who have attained the position of prince by villainy. But Machiavelli is much more limited than Hobbes. Machiavelli puts forward no theory of man or the state. He merely tells, bluntly and amorally, how power may be gained and kept, human nature being what it is, with particular application to the Italy of his day, which he hoped to see united under the rule of a single Italian monarch. Hobbes explains what he thinks man is like, and derives from that the necessity for the state, the nature of true and false religion, and the relationship that should exist between the civil and the ecclesiastical power.

Thomas Hobbes was the son of a Malmesbury vicar. His father was ignorant and quarrelsome, and Thomas was early left to the care of a rich uncle who paid for his education. He was learning Latin and Greek at six, and went up to Magdalen Hall, Oxford, at fourteen. Six years later he left Oxford to become a tutor to William Cavendish, young son of the Earl of Devonshire. Through the Earl he met Bacon; and the Lord Chancellor appreciated Hobbes' help in taking down his thoughts as they walked together, for, as Bacon said, Hobbes was the only companion whose notes showed that he understood his reflections.

For fifteen years Hobbes studied the classics, trying to formulate a philosophy to replace that of Aristotle. In 1628, when Parliament was quarrelling for the first time with Charles I, Hobbes published a translation of Thucydides, a Greek historian with a bias against democracy. Then in 1629 he discovered the fascination of geometry, with its incontrovertible proofs arising from self-evident axioms. From 1634 to 1636 he was on the continent and met Descartes and Galileo among others. On his return to England in 1637, he began to work out his philosophical system.

Seeing the approach of civil war, Hobbes fled to Paris in 1640, where he resumed a place in the circle which included Descartes. However, their philosophical views were divergent, and certain personal differences marred the evenness of their relationship. After 1642 wave after wave of Royalist refugees arrived in Paris. Hobbes, although a staunch supporter of the king, differed widely in outlook from the bulk of the Royalists. He was practically the only upholder of the 'New Philosophy' among them. In consequence, he was suspected of spreading atheism among the queen's court and the Duke of York's household.

In 1651, after the battle of Worcester had proved the Royalist cause hopeless, Hobbes returned to England and submitted to the Council of State, promising to abstain from political activity. It was in this year that he published his famous book, *Leviathan*, which pleased neither party. After the Restoration, Hobbes was in favour at Court for a time, but his reputation for atheism brought him into disfavour with Parliament in 1666, when nerves were tense after the Plague and the Fire of London and some reason for God's wrath was being sought. There was even some talk that the bishops wanted him burned as a heretic! Through Charles II's influence this folly came to nothing. Hobbes died in 1679, at the age of ninety-one, nearly twice the normal lifespan of most men of his times.

Leviathan is far from faultless as a body of philosophy, but is never negligible. Its great virtue is that it clears a way through jungles of confused thinking, by straightforward reasoning built on definitions of the utmost clarity. The book is written in four parts: Of Man, Of Commonwealth, Of a Christian Commonwealth, and Of the Kingdom of Darkness. The first part builds up a psychology of man from considerations of sense mechanism. The second shows how such men must inevitably covenant to form the State, for their own protection, and that the sovereignty thus established must be unlimited in character, or else it is no sovereignty. The third part gives Hobbes' attitude to the Christian religion, in which he stresses that its interpretation must rest in the hands of the State. The last part is devoted to an attack on the Roman Catholic Church, and by implication on other religious bodies, which for Hobbes are chiefly at fault in setting up a rival power to that of the State.

Sense, according to Hobbes, arises through the brain's reaction to a pressure of some substance on the eye, the ear, the nostril, the palate, or the body, which produces motions in the sense organs. Memory and imagination are produced through the persistence of this motion:

When a body is once in motion, it moveth (unless something else hinder it) eternally; and whatsoever hindereth it, cannot in an instant, but in time, and by degrees quite extinguish it: And as we see in the water, though the wind cease, the waves give not over rolling for a long time after; so also it happeneth in that motion, which is made in the internal parts of a man, then, when he sees, dreams, &c. For after the object is removed, or the eye shut, we still retain an image of the thing seen, though more obscure than when we see it. And this is it, the Latins call *Imagination*, from the image made in seeing.

(*Leviathan*, Part I, Ch. 2)

Reasoning derives from speech; and speech is a means of

registering in sound trains of thought, and opinions concerning them. Correct reasoning is simply the correct casting of an account consisting of many definitions. It is through a faulty use of words, says Hobbes, that error arises, and it is then repeated unthinkingly:

By this it appears how necessary it is for any man that aspires to true knowledge, to examine the *Definitions* of former authors; and either to correct them, where they are negligently set down; or to make them himself. For the errors of definitions multiply themselves, according as the reckoning proceeds; and lead men into absurdities, which at last they see, but cannot avoid, without reckoning anew from the beginning; in which lies the foundation of their errors. From whence it happens, that they which trust to books, do as they that cast up many little sums into a greater, without considering whether those little sums were rightly cast up or not; and at last finding the error visible, and not mistrusting their first grounds, know not which way to clear themselves; but spend time fluttering over their books; as birds that entering by the chimney, and finding themselves enclosed in a chamber, flutter at the false light of a glass window, for want of wit to consider which way they came in. . . . For words are wise men's counters, they do but reckon by them: but they are the money of fools, that value them by the authority of an Aristotle, a Cicero, or a Thomas, or any other Doctor whatsoever, if but a man.

(*Leviathan*, Part I, Ch. 4)

Prime sources of confusion, he goes on to say, are self-contradictory words (he instances *incorporeal substance*, and remarks that 'you shall hardly meet with a senseless and insignificant word, that is not made up of some Latin or Greek names'), and words of inconstant meanings. The latter arise through our passions being involved: what one man calls cruelty, another will call justice, and what one man calls wisdom, another will call fear, and so on.

Hobbes says that the passions arise from the three possible

attitudes of men to things: desire, aversion, or indifference.
What a man desires, he calls good; what he hates, he calls
evil. Hope is 'appetite, with an opinion of attaining . . . The
same, without such opinion DESPAIR. *Aversion*, with opinion
of hurt from the object, FEAR. The same, with hope of avoiding that hurt by resistance, COURAGE. Sudden courage
ANGER'. So Hobbes runs through the whole range of human
feelings, not excluding religious feelings. Of these, he says:

> Fear of power invisible, feigned by the mind, or imagined
> from tales publicly allowed, (is) *Religion*; not allowed,
> *Superstition*. And when the power imagined, is truly such as
> we imagine, *True Religion*.
>
> (Leviathan, Part I, Ch. 6)

(This derivation of the meaning of the word *Religion* was
not popular with either bishops or presbyters.)

After discoursing on power and its manifestations, and
making clearer his point about religion, Hobbes asks what
is the natural condition of mankind. Men are fairly equal in
power naturally:

> For as to the strength of body, the weakest has strength
> enough to kill the strongest, either by secret machination,
> or by confederacy with others, that are in the same danger
> with himself.

In wisdom, too, he says, there is a reasonable equality. This
situation, in a state of nature, where there is no power to
keep every man in check, leads to universal war of every
man against every man; and this has many inconveniences:

> In such condition, there is no place for industry; because
> the fruit thereof is uncertain: and consequently no culture
> of the earth, no navigation, nor use of the commodities
> that may be imported by sea; no commodious building; no
> instruments of moving, and removing such things as require
> much force; no knowledge of the face of the earth; no
> account of time; no arts; no letters; no society; and which
> is worst of all, continual fear, and danger of violent death;

and the life of man, solitary, poor, nasty, brutish, and short.
(*Leviathan*, Part I, Ch. 13)

To bear out his reasoning, Hobbes instances how even in civilized countries, men travel armed and in numbers together; they lock their houses against thieves and their chests against their servants. Sovereign states, he says, are still in this condition of universal war, with their forts, garrisons, weapons and spies directed against one another. In such a state of nature, there is no right or wrong, justice or injustice.

To avoid the inconveniences of the natural state, each individual agrees (implicitly or explicitly, voluntarily or under compulsion is of no matter) to give up the right of governing himself to some one man or assembly of men. He agrees to submit to the will and judgement of the ruler, for the common safety.

This done, the multitude so united in one person, is called a *Commonwealth*, in Latin *Civitas*. This is the generation of that great *Leviathan*,* or rather (to speak more reverently) of that mortal god, to which we owe under the Immortal God, our peace and defence. For by this authority, given him by every particular man in the Commonwealth, he hath the use of so much power and strength conferred on him, that by terror thereof, he is enabled to form the wills of them all, to peace at home, and mutual aid against their enemies abroad.

(*Leviathan*, Part II, Ch. 17)

Hobbes recognizes that this Covenant, or social contract, depends on the power of the sword, as well as on agreement. 'Covenants, without the Sword, are but words', as he puts it. Sovereignty, once established, thinks Hobbes, is by its nature absolute. In the sovereign, whether monarch or assembly, reside the rights of peace and war, the rights of censorship over expressions of opinion, control over the

* See Job 41.

laws of property, and the choice of all advisers and ministers. In particular, the control over the militia, and the power of raising taxes, must be with the sovereign. A sovereign who grants away one of these powers is ceasing to be a sovereign.

Of the three types of government which Hobbes recognizes, Monarchy, Aristocracy and Democracy, he much prefers Monarchy, since there is no possibility of faction, though there may be difficulties in the succession. But there is no room in Hobbes' political philosophy for a division of the functions of sovereignty. One of the features of the American constitution is that the Legislature, Executive, and Judicature are in different hands, so that none can establish a tyranny. Hobbes did not imagine that this kind of divided responsibility could lead to other than a faction fight for supreme power, such as had been taking place in England in his days.

Resistance to the sovereign was always wrong, except in two instances, said Hobbes. A man might resist his sovereign in defence of his life, since it was for self-preservation that sovereignty was instituted. (He might not, however, lawfully resist the sovereign in aid of another.) Also, obedience is no longer due to a sovereign who has lost his power to protect his subjects. Hence it was perfectly logical of Hobbes to submit to Cromwell in 1651. Rebellion is wicked until it succeeds. Particularly objectionable is the public proclamation of religious views different from those of the sovereign, which leads inevitably to unrest, since a conflict arises between God's law and the sovereign's. A Christian in a non-Christian state ought to yield outwardly, like Naaman in the temple of Rimmon (II Kings 6). In a Christian state he ought to conform to the interpretations of the ruler, since all Christian systems are based merely on opinion.

There is a great deal to be said for the views of Hobbes. Those who have had the misfortune to live through times of civil war know only too well the dangers of once upsetting the traditional authorities, bad even though they may be. However, there are two serious objections to his political philosophy. One is that the public interest is not usually one and indivisible, for there are party or class interests within a state. The other is that a government may be so bad that even anarchy is preferable to its continuance. John Milton, writing at almost the same time as Hobbes, makes these points, among many others, in defending rebellion, and the execution of Charles I. He, too, advocates a complete removal of political power from churchmen, leaving them only moral suasion to bring men to lead a godly life. There could hardly be two men more opposed in attitude than Milton and Hobbes, but it is surprising how they agree on two basic ideas: that society is machine-like, and capable of improvement; and that governmental functions ought to be out of the hands of priests. (Both these ideas derived ultimately from the discoveries of science.) The ultimate cause of all things, everyone was prepared to admit, was God; but the immediate causes of those things were wheels, not magic.

Milton was a Londoner, not a countryman; and like his fellow-townsmen on the eve of Civil War, was strongly opposed to the power, and even the existence, of bishops. It is difficult in these days of virtual, if not legal, disestablishment, to recapture the animosity of the Puritan against the prelate. Milton's pamphlets of 1641, *Of Reformation Touching Church-Discipline in England* and *The Reason of Church Government Urged against Prelaty* read strangely today, but like the later and better-known *Areopagitica*, urging freedom of the press, and the still later *The Tenure of Kings and Magistrates*, agree remarkably with the atmosphere, if not the conclusions, of Hobbes. To Milton, the moral issue was supreme, to be preferred even above social cohesion. Milton wanted liberty, so that there would be moral virtue in choosing the right course. He wanted freedom of speculation, so that Truth would appear:

F

And though all the winds of doctrine were let loose to play upon the earth, so Truth be in the field, we do injuriously by licensing and prohibiting to misdoubt her strength. Let her and falsehood grapple; who ever knew Truth put to the worse, in a free and open encounter?

(Areopagitica)

How many other things might be tolerated in peace, and left to conscience, had we but charity, and were it not the chief stronghold of our hypocrisy to be ever judging one another. I fear yet this iron yoke of outward conformity hath left a slavish print upon our necks; the ghost of a linen decency yet haunts us . . . Yet if all cannot be of one mind, as who looks they should be? this doubtless is more wholesome, more prudent, and more Christian, that many be tolerated, rather than all compelled. I mean not tolerated Popery, and open superstition, which as it extirpates all religions and civil supremacies, so itself should be extirpate, provided first that all charitable and compassionate means be used to regain the weak and misled: that also which is impious or evil absolutely either against faith or manners no law can possibly permit, that intends not to unlaw itself: but those neighbouring differences, or rather indifferences, are what I speak of, whether in some point of doctrine or of discipline, which though they may be many, yet need not interrupt *the unity of Spirit*, if we could but find among us *the bond of peace*.

(Areopagitica)

Monarchy arose, according to Milton, as according to Hobbes, by social contract; but by one which is revocable:

No man who knows aught, can be so stupid to deny that all men naturally were born free, being the image and resemblance of God himself, and were by privilege above all the creatures, born to command and not to obey: and that they lived so. Till from the root of Adam's transgression, falling among themselves to do wrong and violence, and forseeing that such courses must needs tend to the destruction of them all, they agreed by common league to bind each other from mutual injury, and jointly to defend themselves against any that gave disturbance or opposition to such agreement. Hence came Cities, Towns and Commonwealths. And because no faith in all was found sufficiently binding, they saw it needful to ordain some authority, that might restrain by force and punishment what was violated against peace and common right. This authority and power of self-defence and preservation being originally and naturally in every one of them, and united in them all, for ease, for order, and lest each man should be his own partial Judge, they communicated and derived either to one, whom for the eminence of his wisdom and integrity they chose above the rest, or to more than one whom they thought of equal deserving: the first was called a King; the other Magistrates . . . till the temptation of such a power left absolute in their hands, perverted them at length to injustice and partiality. Then did they . . . invent Laws either framed, or consented to by all, that should confine and limit the authority of those whom they chose to govern them . . . When this would not serve, but that the Law was either not executed, or misapplied, they were constrained from that time, the only remedy left them, to put conditions and take Oaths from all Kings and Magistrates at their first instalment to do impartial justice by Law: who upon those terms and no other, received Allegiance from the people, that is to say, bond or Covenant to obey them in execution of those Laws which they the people had themselves made, or assented to. And this oft-times with express warning, that if the King or Magistrate proved unfaithful to his trust, the people would be disengaged.

(*The Tenure of Kings and Magistrates*)

Thus, to Hobbes, the social contract is irrevocable, for fear of the absolute evil, anarchy; to Milton, the same social contract is dissoluble since it is the servant of justice enshrined in Law. Milton regarded liberty as an aspect of morality; to Hobbes, liberty was merely the choice of action left to the subject by the sovereign, once the latter has been installed as an insurance against the war of all against all. 'As for other liberties, they depend on the silence of the

Law,' says Hobbes. 'In cases where the Sovereign has prescribed no rule, there the subject hath the Liberty to do, or forbear, according to his own discretion.' Neither would allow his supreme good second place to the authority of a priesthood.

It is interesting that although Milton's conclusions are more 'advanced' according to modern ideas, yet his philosophical method is not. He represents, in many ways, a watershed between the old and the new. His impulses were towards liberty and democracy, yet his arguments are based on authority and old writers, rather than on deduction from first principles. Hobbes, on the other hand, comes to a less advanced position through a more scientific method, though his method leans on geometry and lacks the important inductive side which was stressed by Francis Bacon. His conclusions are therefore dependent on the strength of his original assumptions. It is interesting, though, that, just at this time, a philosopher should be found to assert that psychologically and politically man is a machine.

In Hobbes' youth, the opinion that kingship was a status, not an office, was still generally accepted. Shakespeare's plays are full of it. In *Hamlet* we hear 'There's a divinity doth hedge a king'; throughout *Lear* we are shown the dire political, domestic and even meteorological effects which follow a king's renunciation of his status. In *Richard II* the Bishop of Carlisle predicts generations of civil strife, the blood of Englishmen manuring the ground, if the rightful king is deposed; even though he has 'denied himself' and his right to succession, by unjustly depriving the Duke of Hereford of *his* inheritance. Then, the effects were conceived as being basically occult – a far cry from the assumptions of the first lines of Hobbes' book:

Nature (the Art whereby God hath made and governs the World) is by the Art of man, as in many other things, so in this imitated, that it can make an Artificial Animal.

For seeing life is but a motion of limbs, the beginning whereof is in some principal part within; why may we not say, that all Automata (Engines that move themselves by springs and wheels as doth a watch) have an artificial life? For what is the Heart, but a Spring; and the Nerves, but so many Strings; and the Joints, but so many Wheels, giving motion to the whole Body, such as was intended by the Artificer? Art goes yet further, imitating that rational and most excellent work of Nature, Man. For by Art is created that great Leviathan called a Commonwealth, or State (in Latin Civitas) which is but an artificial man; though of greater stature and strength than the natural, for whose protection and defence it was intended.

(*Leviathan*, Introduction)

Philosophical materialism could hardly go farther.

SEVEN

The building of Solomon's house

Francis Bacon was more honoured after his death than in his life. In *The Advancement of Learning* and the *Novum Organum* he had sketched out, roughly and imperfectly it is true, a programme for advancing human knowledge beyond the limits reached by the ancients, through a close connection between scientific research and the craftsman's experience, and through the use of the inductive method. In his *New Atlantis* he gave a fictional account of a scientific academy, such as he believed would lead to startling new discoveries. In the second half of the seventeenth century, academies of this kind were actually founded, and the startling discoveries soon followed.

England, it is true, already boasted Gresham College, but this was an institution for instruction rather than research. Nearer to the academy idea, and even, in fact, earlier than Bacon's fictional House, were certain learned societies in Italy, in particular the Accademia dei Lincei of Rome, of which Galileo was a member. This society had the distinction of being the first to publish a scientific journal (1609). The society had the long-term aim of establishing lay monasteries, with branches all over the world, devoted to scientific research, and in constant communication with one another. After a quarter of a century the group dispersed, following the death of its patron in 1631 and the condemnation of Galileo in 1633.

The first real academy of sciences in the Baconian sense was the successor to the Accademia dei Lincei, the Accademia del Cimento, formed in 1657 under the patronage of the Grand Duke Ferdinand II of Florence, and his brother Leopold, of the famous Medici family. They, and many of the academicians, had been pupils of Galileo, whose opinions, though still under the condemnation of the Church, were nevertheless widely held by the learned. Leopold was himself a skilled experimenter, and the sessions were held in a huge room next to his library. There had been informal meetings of scientists at the palace as early as 1651, but from 1657 to 1667 the academicians, the most brilliant of whom was Borelli (1608–70), pursued a programme of research in physics, chemistry, biology, meteorology, astronomy, and other sciences. They made great advances in measuring techniques, devising thermometers, barometers, hygrometers and clocks. The properties of the vacuum were thoroughly investigated (several pupils of Torricelli were in the Academy), and it was discovered that the vacuum would not support life, but that magnetism, static electricity, the properties of light, and the spherical form of water-drops were not affected. These researches, trivial to us today, were of great importance then, since they made the borderline between matter and space (equated by Descartes) much clearer.

The best known of the scientific academies dating from the mid-century is, of course, the Royal Society of London. This famous body was the successor of informal meetings of experimental scientists which were taking place as early as 1645. These regular meetings, held in the lodgings of various members, appear to have been first suggested by Theodore Haak, a Rhineland German then living in London. Among the regular attenders at these meetings was John Wallis (1616–1703), a brilliant mathematician, who developed the differential calculus, deciphered the papers of Charles I captured at Naseby, and made Thomas

Hobbes look very foolish when the latter attempted to demonstrate the squaring of the circle. Another was Dr. John Wilkins (1614–72), a versatile mathematician and astronomer, who attempted to devise an artificial scientific language and script, which would be international and not subject to the inexactness and emotional overtones of the living or dead languages. Others included Dr. Goddard (1617–74), Cromwell's physician and professor of medicine at Gresham College; and Dr. William Petty, a clothier, keen experimenter and the first to apply statistical methods (somewhat impulsively) to the London bills of mortality.* By 1649 there were two groups, one at Oxford (where many of the fellows who had supported Charles I and the old philosophy had been expelled) and one in London.

On 28 November 1660, a few months after the Restoration of Charles II, the men of science who had gathered to hear a lecture by the able young Christopher Wren (1631–1723) constituted themselves into a definite academy, or as they put it, a 'college for the promoting of Physico-mathematical Experimental Learning'. Dr. Wilkins was appointed chairman, a list of persons fit to be elected members was drawn up, and the following week a formal agreement was signed. Meetings were to be held each Wednesday at Gresham College. (Among the earliest experiments shown to the Society was Boyle's demonstration that the volume of a given mass of gas at a constant temperature was inversely proportional to the pressure on it.) Charles II was interested in the work which had started, and on 15 July 1662 established them by a charter as the Royal Society.

Interest in the corporate development of science had been by no means confined to the experimenters themselves. It was much in the air among the educated of London, whatever their field of study. Abraham Cowley (1618–67),

---

* Dr. Petty had also been formerly an amanuensis of Hobbes, as the latter had been of Bacon.

perhaps the second greatest poet writing in England at that
time, actually published an outline of a scheme for a college
for the advancement of Experimental Philosophy, to be
situated in London, built in the manner of an Oxford
college and endowed with an income of £4,000 per year.
It was a modest scheme, for as he said:

Much might be added, but truly I am afraid this is too
much already for the charity or generosity of this Age to
extend to; and we do not design this after the Model of
Solomon's House in my Lord Bacon (which is a Project
for Experiments that can never be Experimented), but
propose it within such bounds of expense, as have often
been exceeded by the buildings of private citizens.

Cowley pictured the college as consisting of twenty
professors, all single men, of whom four were itinerant, for
a period of at least three years each at a time, one in each
continent (Australia was then unknown). They would
report on the learning and phenomena of their regions. The
remaining sixteen, in residence, were to study and teach

all sorts of Natural Experimental Philosophy, to consist of
the Mathematics, Mechanics, Medicine, Anatomy, Chemistry, the History of Animals, Plants, Minerals, Elements,
etc., Agriculture, Architecture, Art Military, Navigation,
Gardening; the mysteries of all trades, and improvement of
them; the Facture of all Merchandises, all Natural Magic,
or Divination; and briefly all things contained in the
Catalogue of Natural Histories annexed to my Lord Bacon's
Organon.

Sixteen young scholars were to be supported by the establishment, one to each resident professor, as students and
servants. There were besides to be a chaplain, a surgeon,
two laboratory assistants, a man in charge of the animals
and birds, and 'a library-keeper, who is likewise to be

apothecary, druggist, and keeper of instruments, engines, etc.', as well as the customary college servants.

Besides the usual college rooms, there was to be an 'Anatomy-Chamber', a pharmaceutical room, a high tower for use as an observatory, 'great laboratories for chemical operations', deep vaults for underground experiments, a mathematical chamber near the library, and a gallery

adorned with the pictures or statues of all the inventors of any thing useful to human life: as printing, guns, America, etc., and of late in anatomy, the circulation of the blood, the milky veins, and such like discoveries in any art, with short eulogies under the portraitures.

Any professor who made a considerable discovery was to have his place in this gallery; while anyone who made a profitable discovery was to take one-third of the yield, the other two-thirds belonging to the college.

Among the miscellaneous rules Cowley proposes are that the college should give an account every third year of its work, 'in print, in proper and ancient Latin'; that the professors should be inviolable friends, and that uncivil language should be punished by a heavy fine; and, most significantly, that the chaplain 'shall not trouble himself and his auditors with the controversies of divinity, but only teach God in his just commandments, and in his wonderful works'.

A school was to be attached to the college, for pupils of thirteen to seventeen, housing a hundred boys in four classes. Instruction was to be free to all, however rich their parents; and the curriculum, while still leaning heavily on the ancient authors, was to select principally those that dealt with natural phenomena. And finally, as the college prospered it was to establish further schools for poor men's sons of talent,

and shall take care that it shall be done with the same conveniences as are enjoyed even by rich men's children (though they maintain the fewer for that cause), there being nothing of eminent and illustrious to be expected from a low, sordid, and hospital-like education.

Amongst the motives in Cowley's mind in putting forward this scheme was the idea of directing learning away from religious and political controversy. In 1661 the English public was weary of the endless political manœuvres of Presbyterian, Independent, and every species of religious fanatic. Hobbes, only a few years before, had bitterly attacked the universities for breeding religious fanaticism, and regarded Oxford and Cambridge as institutions devised to challenge the secular power. And it is of interest that religion and state affairs were specifically excluded from the domain of the Royal Society. For, as Cowley was to rejoice in a somewhat uninspired ode six years later, the Royal Society concerned itself with things, not words.

The Royal Society, as actually established shortly after Cowley's interesting draft, shows important similarities and differences. In the first place, the early members were largely gentlemen amateurs, with the important exception of Robert Hooke, the first paid curator. The Society had, moreover, no obligation of educating the young, though the Charter granted by Charles II did not exclude the possibility. Also, the royal generosity and patronage did not extend to financial assistance. But the proceedings of the Society were published (though not in proper and ancient Latin) as the *Philosophical Transactions*, the first issue appearing in 1665 – by far the oldest scientific periodical still being published. The Society kept in constant touch with academies and individuals in other parts of the world, and early attained a reputation as a scientific clearing-house for new discoveries in experimental science.

Among the many brilliant men brought together by the new Society, three were outstanding: Wren, Boyle and Hooke. Christopher Wren's architectural career, which blossomed suddenly after the Great Fire of London in 1666, was based on a knowledge of mechanics second to none in his day, but he was equally at home in anatomy, astronomy, chemistry, geometry and botany, as well as other sciences, music and divinity. Although his main energies were turned towards the rebuilding of London, he was for the whole of his life a tireless experimenter and incisive thinker.

Robert Boyle (1627–91) was the son of the first Earl of Cork. He was wealthy, generous, and a sincere Christian. (He spent £5,000 on having the Bible translated into Malay, and gave £2,000 to American missions at a time when missionary activity, except by Jesuits, was at a low ebb.) From the early forties, he had been conducting experiments, chiefly in chemistry, first in his own house, later at Oxford, where he gathered round himself that circle of friends who were later to become part of the Royal Society. To Boyle are due two fundamental discoveries. The first, already briefly mentioned, is Boyle's Law, that under constant conditions of temperature, the pressure of a given mass of gas is inversely proportional to its volume. This law, which is almost exact at low pressures, strongly suggested the atomic structure of matter – a question that had been argued at length in ancient times between the followers and opponents of the philosopher Epicurus. Boyle's other great discovery was a somewhat negative one, but also of great significance. It was that the Aristotelian concept of the four elements had no basis in experimental fact. The alternative theory of chemical composition, which had been advanced by Paracelsus (c. 1493–1540), that the three 'principles' which constituted all 'mixed bodies' were salt, sulphur and mercury (not those precise substances, however, but their philosophical perfections) was likewise exploded by Boyle's work. These two theories, which so strongly suggested that transmutation was possible, had been the basis of much fruitless alchemical research.

Because he rejected 'systems' derived from considerations lying outside experiment, Boyle entitled his greatest work *The Sceptical Chymist* (published 1661). This takes the form of a conversation between three characters, one representing Boyle himself, the others representing the adherents of the Aristotelian and Paracelsian systems. The philosophical difference between the three is brought out strongly. Eleutherius, the Aristotelian, declares:

Aristotle, in his vast and comprehensive intellect, so framed each of his notions, that being curiously adapted into one system, they need not any of them any other defence than that which their mutual coherence gives them: as 'tis in an arch, where each single stone, which if severed from the rest would be perhaps defenceless, is sufficiently secured by the solidity and entireness of the whole fabric of which it is a part. How justly this may be applied to the present case, I could easily show you, were I permitted to declare to you, how harmonious Aristotle's doctrine of the elements is with his other principles of philosophy; and how rationally he has deduced their number from that of the combinations of the four first qualities, from the kinds of simple motion belonging to simple bodies, and from I know not how many other principles and phenomena of nature, which so conspire with his doctrine of the elements, that they mutually strengthen and support each other.

He goes on to exalt deductive reasoning at the expense of inductive: a fundamental point of difference between the old attitude and the new. Deduction, says Eleutherius, is much more high and philosophical.

And therefore the peripatetics have not been very solicitous to gather experiments to prove their doctrines, contenting themselves with a few only, to satisfy those that are not capable of a nobler conviction.

It is needless to follow Boyle's inductive, if somewhat diffuse arguments through the book. He disposes very adequately of the four elements and the three principles, by constant appeal to the laboratory, particularly to the results of distillation experiments. His most important conclusions are that the fire does not, as was thought, break down a compound into its constituent parts; and that the nature and number of the elements is unknown. His clarification of the concept of an element proved to be the foundation of true chemical theory: 'I must not look upon any body as a true principle or element, which is not perfectly homogeneous, but is further resolvable into any number of distinct substances.'

Robert Hooke (1635–1703) was perhaps the most brilliant and versatile scientist of the later seventeenth century, Isaac Newton only excepted. His father was a parson in the Isle of Wight, of no wealth or influence. As a small boy Hooke suffered from poor health, and was educated at home until he was thirteen, when he entered Westminster School. He early showed great talent for making mechanical toys, and at school, and later at Oxford, he showed great speed and talent in mathematical studies. It was at Oxford that he met Dr. John Wilkins, Dr. William Petty and Christopher Wren, members of the Oxford branch of the informal group which later founded the Royal Society, and at Oxford, too, he became an assistant to Robert Boyle. It was natural, in view of his mechanical skill and his talent for significant experiments, that he should be one of the first Fellows appointed, and in November 1662 he was offered the post of Curator of Experiments, his duty being 'to furnish the Society every day they met with three or four considerable experiments, expecting no recompense till the Society get a stock enabling them to give it'. This meant that to a large measure Hooke determined the course of the corporate studies of the whole Society. He was tireless in the invention and improvement of measuring instruments, so fundamental a part of exact science.

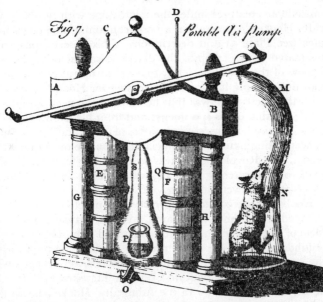

Fig. 7.1 A portable air-pump, of the type used by Hooke and Boyle in the early days of the Royal Society. Here, the behaviour of a rat is being examined, as the air is gradually pumped from its jar.

Amongst Hooke's instruments were the wheel barometer, on which the mercury level could be read off on a circular scale; the anchor escapement, which enabled much more reliable watches to be made; a wind-gauge; a hygrometer which worked from the rolling and unrolling of the beard of a wild oat in different conditions of humidity; an 'arithmetic engine'; telescopic sights; and improvements to almost every instrument he used.

Amongst Hooke's early achievements were his discoveries with the microscope. He discovered the cell-structure of plants, first observed in thin sections of cork. He was the first to observe flies, fleas, ants, and many bacteria and unicellular creatures under the microscope with systematic care. Hooke's *Micrographia*, a book containing fine engravings (see Plate 5) and descriptions of his observations, so fascinated Samuel Pepys, the diarist (also, incidentally, a Fellow of the Royal Society), that he sat up till two in the morning reading it. One of the reasons for Hooke's success with the microscope was that he realized the need for adequate lighting of his specimens; and from his knowledge of optics, devised means, such as globes of water and lenses, for concentrating natural or artificial light on the object under study. The Royal Society was so delighted with Hooke's work on microscopy that he was ordered to bring an observation to every meeting.

Hooke's work constantly preserved a practical bias. He engaged in fundamental research, it is true, but the Baconian ideal of 'the relief of man's estate' directed him in his choice of fundamentals. One of the pressing needs of the time was the improvement of navigational methods, on which his friend Samuel Pepys doubtless kept an interested eye, since he held a high position in the Admiralty. Hooke's Law of Spring, that extension is directly proportional to the extending force, was but one of the discoveries he made in the course of his improvements in measuring time – with an eye towards the difficult problem of determining longitude at sea, which demands the use of a time-piece of extreme refinement.* He invented a sounding-instrument comprising a lead weight, a wooden ball, and a hollow cone, so that the impact of the instrument on the sea-bed touched off a spring, detaching the ball and cone, which surfaced, the latter being more or less filled with water according to the

* This was the first step in a long campaign. Not until 1757 was there a time-piece sufficiently accurate for the purpose, despite the offer of a large prize by the Admiralty for a solution to the longitude problem. One of Gulliver's reasons for wanting to be an immortal Struldbrug, it will be recalled, was that he would live to see the 'discovery of the longitude'.

depth. For astronomical observations he devised a clock-driven telescope. He was also interested in map projections and other cartographical problems, and helped to produce a new atlas which appeared in 1680. Finally, it deserves mention that Hooke had a very fair idea of the laws of gravitation, by which the movements of the heavenly bodies might be accurately predicted, though he did not have sufficient mathematical skill to anticipate Newton.

The career of Hooke shows not only the achievements of a versatile genius at a favourable time for science, but also the beneficial results of such institutions as the Royal Society. For Hooke was not a wealthy man. He, and the other Fellows, benefited from the common stock of instruments gradually being accumulated at Gresham College. Instrument-making is expensive even today; in the 1660's it was prohibitively costly for all except the favoured few like Robert Boyle. Besides, there was the constant interchange of new ideas between scientists. Wren suggested a kind of weather-clock to record the temperature, pressure, humidity, wind direction and velocity, and rainfall on a paper drum each quarter hour; Hooke made it, and the Society paid for it. The Society was also able to sponsor scientific publications: not only *Philosophical Transactions*, but also such books as John Evelyn's *Sylva* (a treatise on forestry), Hooke's *Micrographia*, and Francis Willughby's *History of Fishes*, an elaborate and expensive volume which almost bankrupted the Society but was a notable event in zoology.

In 1666 France followed the English lead through the establishment of the Académie des Sciences. This society traces its origin back to the informal gatherings round a mathematically minded priest, Mersenne (1588–1648), an intimate friend of Descartes and a correspondent of many leading European scientists and philosophers, including Galileo and Hobbes. Colbert, the far-sighted minister of Louis XIV, saw the advantages to be gained from giving

G

financial assistance to this group, which had retained its identity after Mersenne's death, and from its foundation until Colbert's death in 1683 the Académie produced fine work, though not of the brilliance of its English rival. There followed a period of decline until the end of the century, when the society revived, and today it still exists as one of the oldest scientific academies in the world. From its earliest days it lacked the independence of the Royal Society, but it was able to undertake far more expensive pieces of research, for instance an astronomical expedition to Cayenne, where it was found that a pendulum did not vibrate at the same rate as in Paris – an observation which led to the discovery that the earth is slightly flattened at the poles.

The advances in human knowledge, which had been stimulated by joint research, were changing man's whole idea of the universe. It was Isaac Newton who was to cement the new philosophy; but even before his work, the Aristotelian view of life had been destroyed in detail.

EIGHT

And all was light

Since the publication of his work, Sir Isaac Newton has justly received the praise of every age as the greatest scientist of all time. His genius it was which was able to enunciate universal laws of motion, obeyed by stars as by stones, living beings, or specks of dust. The universe suddenly became predictable. Alexander Pope, writing in 1732, proposed as his epitaph the well-known lines:

> Nature and Nature's laws lay hid in night:
> God said, 'Let Newton be!' and all was light.

And throughout his works Pope rejoices that the universe operates by general, not partial laws, and warns his readers not to expect private miracles:

> When the loose mountain trembles from on high,
> Shall gravitation cease if you go by?
> *(Essay on Man)*

Fifty years later Dr. Samuel Johnson remarked as a matter of common knowledge that although mathematical learning was more widely diffused than formerly nobody in his age could rival Newton. In fact his achievements were so tremendous that, as Bertrand Russell says,

The triumph was so complete that Newton was in danger of becoming another Aristotle, and imposing an insuperable barrier to progress. In England, it was not till a century after his death that men freed themselves from his authority sufficiently to do important original work in the subjects of which he had treated.

(*History of Western Philosophy*)

The only two dissenting voices to the chorus of universal praise are those of William Blake, whose cloudy mysticism had no room for mathematical demonstration, and Dean Swift, whose bitter satire found victims through all times and places.*

Newton was born in 1642, not far from Grantham, the child of farming parents. At the age of eighteen, he went up to Trinity College, Cambridge, where he came in contact with Isaac Barrow, a gifted mathematician. Barrow early recognized Newton's talent, and in 1667 he was elected a Fellow of Trinity College. In 1669 Newton succeeded Barrow as Lucasian Professor of Mathematics in the University. It was only in 1671 that the Royal Society came to learn of Newton's skill, when news of the reflecting

* *Gulliver's Travels* (first published 1726) contains an amusing parody of the Royal Society as a whole, under the name of the Grand Academy of Ladago, where projects such as those for the extraction of sunbeams from cucumbers, or the calcination of ice into gunpowder were carried on. The efforts of one Ladago astronomer were directed to making a sundial, to be placed on the town hall weathercock, so calculated that the annual and diurnal motions of the earth would counteract the accidental turnings of the wind! Gulliver is later given the opportunity of summoning the spirits of Aristotle and Descartes. Surprisingly, both come off with honour, Aristotle admiring the system of Descartes, though exploded:

'He predicted the same fate to attraction, whereof the present learned are such zealous asserters. He said that the new systems of nature were but new fashions, which would vary in every age; and even those who pretend to demonstrate them from mathematical principles would flourish but a short period of time, and be out of vogue when that was determined.'

Also, as a tribute to the disputatious nature of some of the Fellows, he makes Gulliver present three Brobdingnagian wasp-stings to 'Gresham College', or the Royal Society. But Swift's enmity is, in its way, as considerable a compliment as the praise of the rest of mankind.

telescope spread from Cambridge to London. On being asked to show the instrument to the Society, he made them one, with a concave mirror two inches across and a tube nine inches long, which is still preserved. Newton was elected to the Royal Society, and asked to give a written account of the invention. Newton did as asked, adding his reasons for inventing the telescope, reasons which staggered the Royal Society. For the young man had solved a very old problem: the nature of white and coloured light. He had, moreover, kept the discovery by him for some years, without bothering to tell anyone!

The refracting telescope, as invented sixty years before and used to such effect by Galileo, suffered from one great disadvantage: the images had coloured edges. It was recognized that this phenomenon was related to the coloured edges to objects seen through a glass prism, an observation that had been made in Roman times. But it was left to Newton to give the explanation, and to give it, moreover, in an exact mathematical form. For Newton had two enormous advantages over the other thinkers who might have attempted to solve the problem: he was the most brilliant mathematician of his age; and he was not led astray by the persisting relics of medieval philosophy, which suggested that 'obviously' white light was simple and colour a complication, a secondary quality.

By a series of experiments with prisms Newton showed that the reverse was true, that coloured light is simple, while white light is a mixture. He extended the old experiment of passing a beam of light through a glass prism to produce the band of colours we now know as the spectrum: he re-combined the colours with a second prism the other way round, producing white light again (Fig. 8.1).

Next, he extended the traditional experiment in a different way. He allowed one colour of the spectrum to pass on to a second prism, while the others were intercepted by a wooden screen. The coloured beam was refracted in the

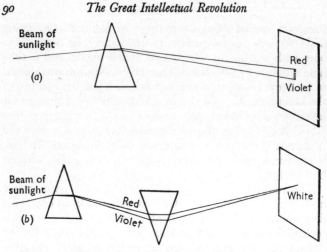

Fig. 8.1 (a) The traditional experiment; *(b)* the recombination of the colours.

same way, and to the same amount, as when it had been separated out of the white light, but it remained the same colour (Fig. 8.2).

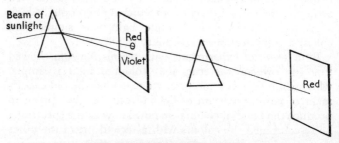

Fig. 8.2 The crucial experiment.

He further extended the discovery to work with lenses by a simple but beautiful experiment. He took a piece of card, painted one half red, the other half blue. He wound a black cotton thread round the card, illuminated it as strongly as he could, and focused the image of the threads on to a piece of white paper. It proved impossible to get a clear image of the lines on the red *and* those on the blue. One or other would always be out of focus. As blue light is bent more than red, the explanation is simple (Fig. 8.3).

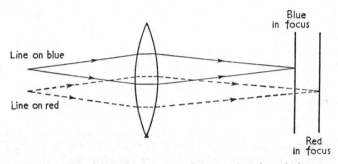

Fig. 8.3 Newton's explanatory experiment on the coloured edges of images seen through a lens.

Newton gave a mathematical treatment to the whole problem of refraction, and the different refrangibility of light rays of different colours; and this work was the basis of modern optics. He showed that whatever shape of surface one gave to a lens, there would be bound to be coloured edges.

For this reason he invented the reflecting telescope (see Plate 7 and Fig. 8.4). The angles of reflection, unlike those of refraction, are the same for all colours. He realized that a concave mirror produced the same kind of image as a convex lens, and soon made a telescope no more than six inches long, with a mirror one inch across, which was capable of magnifying forty diameters. It was the ancestor of the great 200-inch reflecting telescope on Mount Palomar, used today for the most advanced astronomical research.

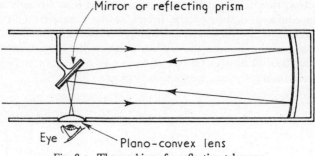

Fig. 8.4 The working of a reflecting telescope.

The Royal Society was delighted with both the instrument and the research on the properties of light.* What the Society did not know, because Newton diffidently had not told them, was that he had already made a mathematical demonstration of the laws of motion, in particular, the famous Law of Gravity. The well-known apple incident (which really happened) took place in the autumn of 1666. Newton had that winter proved that every movement in the universe could be explained if it is assumed that:

1. Every piece of matter in the universe remains at rest, or moves at a constant velocity in a straight line, unless acted on by an outside impressed force.

2. Change of motion is proportional to the motive force impressed, and is made in the direction in which that force is impressed.

3. Every action has an equal and opposite reaction.

4. Every piece of matter in the universe attracts every

* This was the reaction of the Royal Society as a whole, but a series of objections was put forward, first by Robert Hooke, then by Francis Linus, mathematical professor at Liège. Newton was much annoyed by the rather unskilful objections of Linus, and regretted making his discoveries public. It was probably through his hatred of controversy, amounting almost to a persecution mania, that Newton delayed the publication of his *Opticks* until 1704, though nearly all his work on light had been carried out by 1675.

other piece with a force proportional to the product of their masses and inversely proportional to the square of the distance between them.

In particular, it could be shown why Kepler's laws of planetary motion worked.

The idea of a gravitational force inherent in every heavenly body was not a new one. Even before Copernicus several philosophers had contradicted Aristotle's idea that all heavy objects tended towards one place, and one place only, the centre of the universe, which was also the centre of the earth. Copernicus himself took the view that there were local gravitational systems, to parry the objections of those who claimed that if the sun were the centre of the universe loose objects on the earth would fall into it. The strongest objections to attraction theories were the objections to the idea of action across a vacuum, or action at a distance at all. Gilbert's work on magnetism did much to prepare the scientific mind for the novel concept. Kepler suggested that the planets were propelled forwards by a force from the sun, and held in by an attractive force; and this attractive force he visualized as mutual. (His first idea, though incorrect, was intended to explain why the outer planets moved slower than the inner ones.)

In Newton's own time, John Wilkins suggested that each heavenly body had an attractive force extending for, say, twenty miles up. Thus if a traveller were once able to rise beyond this point, the slightest of forces would carry him to the moon or elsewhere. Descartes and his followers had postulated vortices of invisible matter which carried the planets round. His was the chief non-gravitational theory in the field; but by the time Milton was writing *Paradise Lost*, gravitational theories seem to have been the chief alternative to the Ptolemaic idea that the earth was at the centre. For in Book VIII, when Adam is inquiring concerning celestial motions, Raphael replies that God has concealed the answer,

>   . . . perhaps to move
> His laughter at their quaint opinions wide
> Hereafter, when they come to model Heav'n
> And calculate the stars, how they will wield
> The mighty frame, how build, unbuild, contrive
> To save appearances, how gild the Sphere
> With Centric and Eccentric scribbled o'er,
> Cycle and Epicycle, Orb in Orb.

He replies that Adam may take his pick:

>   What if the Sun
> Be centre to the World, and other stars
> *By his attractive virtue and their own*
> Incited, dance about him various rounds?
> Their wandering course now high, now low, then hid,
> Progressive, retrograde, or standing still,
> In six thou seest, and what if sev'nth to these
> The planet Earth, so stedfast though she seem,
> Insensibly three different motions move?
> Which else to several Spheres thou must ascribe
> Moved contrary with thwart obliquities.

Whereupon Raphael proposes that Adam should take up some different kind of research!

Ironically enough, Newton was producing the answer at the same time that Milton was pronouncing it unanswerable! Borelli, Huygens and Hooke were also at work, with Edmond Halley and Christopher Wren collaborating later. Experiments at great heights and at great depths were being made in an attempt to measure differences in the gravitational force. The Royal Society group were pooling information, and discussing the problem constantly, while Newton, at Cambridge or at home in Lincolnshire, was working by himself. Having drawn his conclusion, the famous inverse square law, he refrained from publishing, partly through a natural diffidence and fear of controversy, partly because he was dissatisfied about certain minor details in his analysis.

The chief of these details was the problem whether it was correct to assume that the whole mass of the moon, or the earth, was concentrated at its centre. If so, planetary sizes could be neglected, and the already complicated problem could be simplified to one of the attraction between lumps, instead of an infinite number of petty attractions between atoms. The attraction of the earth for a falling stone is, after all, the resultant of the attraction of all the particles of the earth, some near, some far. Did this resultant equal the attractive force there would be if the whole of the earth's mass were concentrated at the centre? That this was so, he was only able to prove nearly twenty years later, when he had further developed his 'fluxions' or calculus.

It was early in 1684 that Halley, Wren and Hooke were engaged on the problem. Hooke was already convinced that the key to the problem of planetary motion was that the force between pieces of matter was inversely proportional to the square of the distance between them, but he had not the mathematics to prove that this law would result in planets following an elliptical course. In August 1684, Halley visited Cambridge to ask Newton what he thought. What, Halley asked, would a planetary course be, assuming the inverse square law to be true. Newton immediately replied that it would be an ellipse, and that he had worked the problem out. Newton later sent his papers to Halley, incorporating the most recent astronomical observations, and covering the details he had left unsolved in the sixties. He was enabled to make these calculations by a method he had himself evolved, which is now known as the calculus.

Halley pressed Newton to publish his discoveries, and even paid for the expenses of printing, as the Royal Society's funds had then been sadly depleted by the publication of that beautifully illustrated but very expensive book about fishes. But the Royal Society gave its official blessing to Newton's book, and the name of the President of the Royal

Society, Samuel Pepys, the famous diarist, appears on the title page with that of Newton himself.

The title of the book, which appeared in 1687, is *Philosophiae Naturalis Principia Mathematica*, now called simply Newton's *Principia*. It is perhaps the most important volume the world has ever seen, and not only for scientists. It is also an extremely difficult one to follow, since Newton 'translated' the calculus he had used in making his discoveries into a geometrical notation which would be understood by his readers – or at least some of them!

Descartes' idea that the planets were carried round by whirlpools of subtle matter was demolished very convincingly. Newton showed that the mathematics of whirlpools simply would not account for such elementary observations as the length of planetary years, or the observed orbits. Newton accounted for all the current gravitational problems, such as the behaviour of the pendulum; he showed how the orbits of the planets and their satellites agreed with his laws, showed how to calculate the masses of heavenly bodies, and even predicted that the earth would be found to be slightly flattened at the poles. He treated the problem of the tides and showed how they were caused by the attraction of the moon and sun (the latter determining how high the tide will be by assisting or hindering the attraction of the moon).

Throughout the book Newton denies that he is suggesting *causes* for the phenomena he discusses. He gives mathematical laws by which they act, but does not give occult 'reasons'. Critics of less learning than he often irritated Newton by their misunderstanding of his position. He was always over-sensitive, and often believed, wrongly, that he was being persecuted; in particular, he quarrelled with Robert Hooke. Eventually he abandoned all scientific work because of the disputes it involved him in. These he often took as personal reflections.

The Newtonian method is an inductive one, quite unlike

the deductive process of Descartes. Descartes had, like many others, been led astray by the success of the deductive method in Euclid's geometry, where on *assuming* that points have position but no size, lines length but no breadth, and so on, all the theorems follow. This led him to attempt to erect a universal, all-embracing deductive system from a number of assumptions which were necessarily, by the nature of the method, very questionable. Newton's method, and the method of scientists generally, is to work towards the establishment of *limited* chains of deduction. The work starts with observation, checked, repeated and tabulated. From the information, a general rule is formulated. Assuming the general rule, a number of consequences may be predicted, and these are to be tested by further experiment. Newton detested what he called *hypotheses*, using the word in a rather old-fashioned way, to mean anything not derived from the phenomena. He aimed at description rather than explanation.

His attitude is well illustrated by his own statements on method. In the *Principia* he enunciates four Rules of Reasoning, which are as follows:

1. We are to admit no more causes of natural things than such as are both true and sufficient to explain their appearances.

This is simply a restatement of a principle well known in medieval times.

2. To the same natural effects, we must, as far as possible, assign the same causes.

He gives several instances, such as remarking that we must consider the cause of the falling of stones in both Europe and America to be the same.

3. The qualities of bodies, which admit neither intensification nor remission of degrees, and which are found to belong to all bodies within the reach of our experiments,

are to be esteemed the universal qualities of all bodies whatsoever.

The most important instance of the application of this rule is in consideration of the movements of heavenly bodies: inertia and gravitational attraction are observed in the solar system, and are therefore to be deemed the properties of all matter, observable or not.

4. In experimental philosophy we are to look upon propositions inferred by general induction from phenomena as accurately or very nearly true, notwithstanding any contrary hypotheses that may be imagined, till such time as other phenomena occur, by which they may either be made more accurate, or liable to exceptions.

In other words, experiment, not imagination, is to be the test.

We see in Newton's *Opticks* what he thought of the Aristotelian approach:

These principles I consider, not as occult Qualities, supposed to result from the specific Forms of things, but as general Laws of Nature, by which the things themselves are formed; their truth appearing to us by phenomena, though their causes be not yet discovered. For these are manifest qualities, and their causes only are occult. And the Aristotelians gave the name of occult qualities, not to manifest qualities, but to such qualities only as they supposed to lie hid in bodies, and to be the unknown causes of manifest effects: Such as would be the Causes of Gravity, and of magnetic and electric attractions, and of fermentations, if we should suppose that these forces or actions arose from Qualities unknown to us, and uncapable of being discovered and made manifest. Such occult Qualities put a stop to the improvement of natural philosophy, and therefore of late years have been rejected. To tell us that every species of things is endowed with an occult specific Quality by which it acts and produces manifest effects, is to tell us nothing: but to derive two or three general Principles of Motion from phenomena, and afterwards to tell us how the properties and actions of all corporeal things follow from those manifest Principles, would be a very great step in philosophy, though the causes of those principles were not yet discovered: And therefore I scruple not to propose the principles of motion above-mentioned, they being of very general extent, and leave their causes to be found out.

Newton, too, was very clear about the distinction between words and things, like Bacon and Hobbes.

Newton was prepared to agree that induction was a less rigorous demonstration of truth than deduction. But the scope of deduction is limited, whereas the laws derived from induction may be applied more widely. At the end of the *Opticks*, Newton says:

As in mathematics, so in natural philosophy, the investigation of difficult things by the method of analysis, ought ever to precede the method of composition. This analysis consists in making experiments and observations, and in drawing general conclusions from them by induction, and admitting of no objections against the conclusions, but such as are taken from experiments, or other certain truths. For hypotheses are not to be regarded in experimental philosophy. And although the arguing from experiments and observations by induction be no demonstration of general conclusions; *yet it is the best way of arguing which the nature of things admits of*, and may be looked upon as so much the stronger, by how much the induction is more general. And if no exception occur from phenomena, the conclusion may be pronounced generally. But if at any time afterwards any exception shall occur from experiments, it may then begin to be pronounced with such exceptions as occur. By this way of analysis we may proceed from compounds to ingredients, and from motions to the forces producing them; and in general, from effects to their causes, and from particular causes to more general ones, till the argument end in the most general. This is the method of analysis: And the synthesis consists in assuming the causes discovered, and established as principles, and by them explaining the phenomena proceeding from them, and proving the explanations.

It is interesting that the great philosopher of Newton's time, John Locke (1632–1704), is just as contemptuous of large hypothetical speculations. He is pre-eminently the philosopher of the commonsense approach, content with limited chains of reasoning, well established and supported by experience, rather than the more ambitious 'system', which, when consistent with itself, leads to conclusions unacceptable to common sense. His empiricism, as it is called, had a very large influence on the eighteenth-century attitude to the world, both directly, and through the work of Voltaire. Locke's chief work is the *Essay Concerning Human Understanding*. He says that the occasion for his writing this book was a discussion with friends (probably on principles of morality and revealed religion) when they 'found themselves quickly at a stand by the difficulties that rose on every side'. Locke decided that their dilemma arose because they had not considered what objects their understandings were fitted to deal with. He says:

If we can find out how far the understanding can extend its view, how far it has faculties to attain certainty, and in what cases it can only judge and guess, we may learn to content ourselves with what is attainable by us in this state . . . How short soever their knowledge may come of an universal or perfect comprehension of whatsoever is, it yet secures their great concernments that they have light enough to lead them to knowledge of their Maker, and the sight of their own duties. Men may find matter sufficient to busy their heads and employ their hands with variety, delight, and satisfaction, if they will not boldly quarrel with their own constitution, and throw away the blessings their hands are filled with, because they are not big enough to grasp everything.

Locke disagreed with those philosophers (such as Descartes) who believed that certain propositions were inborn.

He believed that all knowledge, even such elementary propositions as 'nothing can both be and not be', must arise from experience: in the first place sense observations, and then the reflection of the mind on that assembled data, and the observation of its own working. This was quite a new doctrine.

He did not demand the utmost rigour of demonstration of a fact before he was prepared to believe it. He distinguished three kinds of knowledge: (*a*) knowledge of oneself, from intuition; (*b*) knowledge of the existence of God, through rational demonstration (Newton's picture of the universe was very favourable to some of the traditional arguments for the existence of a deity); and (*c*) knowledge of the world, which arises through sensation. But many of the propositions on which we act, he says, are far from certain, and we must use our judgements to assess probabilities.

It is not in every case we can be sure that we have all the particulars before us, that in any way concern the question; and that there is no evidence behind, and yet unseen, which may cast the probability on the other side, and outweigh all that at present seems to preponderate with us. And yet we are forced to determine ourselves on the one side or other. The conduct of our lives, and the management of our great concerns, will not bear delay.

But this willingness to weigh probabilities, and accept tentative answers, presupposes toleration of others' views.

His attitude is basically that of Newton's, applied in a rather different field. 'It is the best way of arguing that the nature of things admits of', as Newton said. Locke's particular pronouncements, although his views on government and education, as well as on philosophy, did much to shape developments in Britain and Europe, are of less importance than the temper of his mind. His was the sort of attitude that encouraged parliamentary democracy, freedom of worship, and liberal ideas generally. An outlaw for five

H

years, the victim of intolerance, he was yet able to advocate toleration when his friends gained political power in the Revolution of 1688, and had the chance to retaliate on their opponents.

Locke's views were, however, unfriendly to the life of the emotions. He exalted judgement at the expense of what was then called wit. Metaphor and allusion fed the fancy, he maintained, and discouraged the mind from looking into the truth of what was propounded. It is understandable, in the circumstances of his time, that his condemnation of reliance on the feelings should have been an acceptable viewpoint. The great successes of the age were those of reason, not emotion.

For instance, reason took the terror out of comets. Edmond Halley (1656–1742) applied the Newtonian laws with conspicuous success to their tracks. From earliest times comets had seemed mysterious and terrible to mankind. In shape a comet appears like a rather woolly star, with a long, luminous, remarkable tail, the whole looking like a flame or a sword. They were associated with wars, plagues, disasters and the deaths of rulers. In 1665 and 1666 public alarm in London was increased by the appearance of two comets, the first associated with the Plague, the second with the Great Fire. (Even today, the superstitious feelings remain to some extent among the general public, who feel that there is something not quite proper about a comet, and that evil is bound to accompany the appearance of a conspicuous one.*) The one beneficial effect they were believed to produce was an improvement in the wine made from the grapes of comet years. Aristotle had regarded comets as the effects of fire in the regions below the moon, and it will be remembered how Tycho Brahe proved that certain comets were

---

* The feelings are always justified, too, for there is quite enough disaster and death in the world to attach itself to any comet. I forget just what the brilliant comet of early June 1957 was supposed to have done, but I remember many who felt very nervous about it.

beyond the moon. But it was Halley who brought the comet into the realms of ordinary, predictable nature.

He did this by showing that the tracks of the bright comets of the years 1531, 1607 and 1682 were practically the same. He showed that these three appearances must have been of the same comet, which had travelled round an elliptical orbit like a planet, but an orbit so elongated that seventy-six years were needed for it to pass round the sun. A comet passes the sun end of its orbit in a few weeks, but it moves very slowly indeed round the rest of its course. (A brief consideration of Kepler's Second Law will indicate why.) Halley maintained that the great comets of 1305 and 1456 had been previous appearances of the same comet, and predicted that it would return in 1758. It was observed right at the end of that year, and both Newton and Halley were shown to be right.

Certainties of this kind were inimical to the use of large emotional appeals in, say, the drama. Shakespeare had spoken of comets with effect right at the beginning of his trilogy of *Henry VI*, in connection with the early death of the warrior-king, Henry V:

> Hung be the heavens with black, yield day to night!
> Comets, importing change of times and states
> Brandish your crystal tresses in the sky
> And with them scourge the bad revolting stars
> That have consented unto Henry's death!

And when, in *Julius Cæsar*, he made Calpurnia warn:

> When beggars die, there are no comets seen;
> The heavens themselves blaze forth the death of princes.

For a dramatist to have rhapsodized in this way, after the publication of the *Principia* and Halley's work on comets, would have been ridiculous. Poets were left with no supernatural machinery, unless used in joke only.

The general clearing of the air of magical concepts also helped England to get rid of James II in 1688. The Divine

Right of Kings was a serious matter in his grandfather's time; after the work of the Royal Society, Hobbes and others, it looked rather ridiculous. Locke was pre-eminently the philosopher of the Glorious Revolution, and worked hard in its intellectual defence. Newton himself served as one of the Members of Parliament for Cambridge University in 1689 and 1690, and there is no doubt that his sympathies were with William III and good sense, as against James II and Divine Right. After this time Newton was taking less and less part in scientific work. In 1696 he was made Warden, and in 1699 Master, of the Mint; and he supervised a difficult recoinage operation, with which John Locke, too, was associated.

It seems strange that such a man as Newton, after setting the tone for an age, should have turned his back so resolutely on the source of his fame. In 1703 he was elected President of the Royal Society, after Hooke's death. In 1704 his *Opticks* was published, though most of the work in it had been done years before. In his old age he turned to religious matters, including involved systems of biblical chronology. He also detected two early corruptions introduced into the text of the Bible. His mental powers remained as sharp as they had ever been to his death in 1727, but for the last thirty years of his life they were only very seldom, and then unwillingly, engaged in scientific work. It is remarkable that such a man should have almost casually, as it were, thrown off such a book as the *Principia*.

For Newton's work was the culmination of the intellectual revolution of the seventeenth century. Educated, but non-scientific thought is to this day based on Newtonian discoveries. Facts which fit in with what Newton pronounced to be the normal course of nature we regard as needing no further explanation. We may argue about the creation of the universe, but not about its day-to-day operation. On his work depends our whole vision of the ordinary. But in praising him we must not forget the little band of predecessors who made his work possible, nor the men of business or action whose needs demanded the right answers to fundamental problems, instead of merely pretty ones.

NOTE ON NEWTON'S VIEW OF A PLANETARY ORBIT

Non-scientific readers may not readily see how Newton combined the ideas of gravity and the planetary orbit, especially as the treatment is highly mathematical. But the following is an attempt at a qualitative explanation.

The course of a cannon-ball or other projectile is well known: it is a parabola (Fig. 8.5):

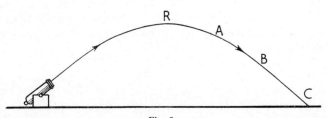

Fig. 8.5

The cannon-ball's vertical motion slows down to a point of rest *R*, and then accelerates in its fall from *A* to *B* to *C*. Now a satellite is in the same position as a projectile that is constantly falling towards the earth, but never getting there, and at the same time accelerating on approaching the earth, or decelerating as it moves away. If the earth were not there, the projectile would move steadily in a straight line for ever; and so would a satellite. But in the presence of the earth, both fall freely. The projectile hits the earth; the satellite swings round it (Fig. 8.6).

Now on its elliptical orbit a satellite stores up speed as it approaches the earth, because it has fallen towards the earth.

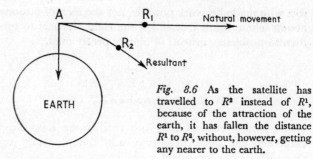

Fig. 8.6 As the satellite has travelled to R^2 instead of R^1, because of the attraction of the earth, it has fallen the distance R^1 to R^2, without, however, getting any nearer to the earth.

This speed is sufficient to carry it *away* from the earth on the *other* side of its orbit, when of course it slows down, just as the cannon-ball does when rising from the earth. The same consideration applies to an orbiting space-craft. The pilot is weightless, not because he is outside the attraction of the earth, but because he is in a state of free fall towards the earth.

NINE

The death of metaphor

The Great Intellectual Revolution has now been traced from its first beginnings in the application of exact methods to problems arising from an improved technology, to the synthesis achieved by Sir Isaac Newton. On the way it has been possible to consider some of the more important philosophical, theological and political effects of the beginning of science. In this chapter an attempt will be made to trace the effects of the revolution on literature, effects which are still far from being worked out. The state of scientific knowledge has had a considerable effect on writers. What Shakespeare could write with conviction and sincerity would have been impossible for Milton and unthinkable for Pope, though the literary talents of all three were, if not equal, certainly of the same high order. Shakespeare ranks as the greatest of the three at least partly because his career fell at a fortunate period for the theatre, an optimistic period in the national life, at the beginning of a great age for the English language, and *before* the Great Intellectual Revolution. At the time he wrote, metaphor had a force it could never attain after the work of Newton.

An analogy today may be one of two kinds, scientific or literary. The first kind serves as a scientist's working model. The old picture of atoms as being perfectly round, perfectly hard, perfectly elastic balls, moving at various speeds, was a model of this kind. So was Rutherford's later picture of a heavy atomic nucleus, positively charged, with a number of planetary, light electrons circling round it. This type of analogy is used in summarizing the knowledge gained from experiments, and suggesting further properties of the object for which it may be tested in later experiments. If the predictions are fulfilled, the model is retained; if the predictions are not fulfilled, the model is either modified or abandoned. A literary analogy, usually a metaphor, has quite different purposes. It is designed to impress the reader with the truth of a statement by a happy comparison directed at the feelings. It is a very temporary affair compared with the scientific model, which is in permanent use for making calculations and predictions until it is superseded. Moreover, the metaphor may illustrate or adorn an argument, but it is not one in itself. In other words, it is not to be taken really seriously.

Yet before the Great Intellectual Revolution, these two kinds of analogy were nearly, if not completely, one. The moral order was imagined to be intimately related to the physical world at every point. When Shakespeare makes Ulysses argue for proper military discipline, on the grounds that the sun is in a commanding position among the planets (see page 11), he is not merely putting forward a pretty illustration, he is making what he believed to be a correct scientific statement of the nature of the universe. It was part of the divine order of things that the sun should rule the planets, and that Agamemnon should rule the Greeks; and the failure of one or the other to command was likely to have far-reaching repercussions in the world at large. Vividness of metaphor, down to the early seventeenth century, could be something more than a memorable assault on the feelings. The rise of science led to a separation of reason from emotion; and, naturally enough, an age of prose followed an age of poetry.

Even prose, before the mid-seventeenth century, was colourful and poetic in a way which, by the time of Swift and Addison, would have seemed insincere. A choice collection of examples of the pre-scientific use of analogy in argument may be found in that much-derided, but little-read book, Lyly's *Euphues*, first published in 1579, and in its day a successful and admired book, both for its style and for its moral content. It is significant that the book was frequently reprinted until 1636, after which date it lost favour among general readers, and became merely a literary curiosity. As an instance of its style the following may be quoted, some of the hero's reflections when he has found himself deceived in love by a Neapolitan beauty, and has resolved to devote his talents to study instead of courtship.

If wit be employed in the honest study of learning, what thing so precious as wit? if in the idle trade of love, what thing more pestilent than wit?

The proof of late hath been verified in me, whom nature hath endued with a little wit, which I have abused with an obstinate will: most true it is that the thing the better it is, the greater is the abuse, and that there is nothing but through the malice of man may be abused.

Doth not the fire (an element so necessary that without it man cannot live) as well burn the house, as burn in the house, if it be abused? Doth not treacle as well poison as help, if it be taken out of time? Doth not wine, if it be immoderately taken, kill the stomach, inflame the liver, mischief the drunken? Doth not physic destroy if it be not well tempered? Doth not law accuse if it be not rightly interpreted? Doth not divinity condemn if it be not faithfully construed? Is not poison taken out of the honeysuckle by the spider? venom out of the rose by the canker? dung out of the maple tree by the scorpion? Even so the greatest wickedness is drawn out of the greatest wit, if it be abused by will, or inveigled with women.

But seeing I see mine own impiety, I will endeavour myself to amend all that is past, and be a mirror of Godliness hereafter. The rose though a little it be eaten with the canker, yet being distilled yieldeth sweet water: the iron though fretted with the rust, yet being burnt in the fire shineth brighter: and wit, although it hath been eaten with the canker of his own conceit, and fretted with the rust of vain love, yet being purified in the still of wisdom, and tried in the fire of zeal, will shine bright and smell sweet in the nostrils of all young novices.

The various phenomena of nature he speaks of were serious arguments for the point he was making – not, as we are apt to think today, an overloaded assemblage of ornament, like the worst kind of Victorian drawing-room. His comparisons are chosen to establish basic truths of nature, from which his own experiences can be deduced.

Indeed, Aristotle's philosophy, as understood in medieval times and later, invited union of thought and feeling. The concept that earth, air, fire and water had 'natural places' is very close to a moral concept. The Chain of Being was a direct comparison between a feudal order and the world of nature. St Thomas Aquinas had said that the universe was a hierarchy of creatures ordered to perfection in their several kinds. A poet thus did not have to *pretend* that a natural phenomenon had a lesson for man, he could proclaim outright that it had, and no one would deny it.

The new observations which were later to lead to the abandonment of the systems of Aristotle and Ptolemy were, at first, employed by writers in the same way as the old facts had been. Especially, one may find in the poems of John Donne, and the later so-called 'metaphysical' poets, an astoundingly detailed analysis, intellectual and emotional at once, of what we would call scientific facts. The sermons of John Donne are also an especially good place in which to search for these late examples of the unified worldview. The following was preached in 1626:

Upon this earth, a man cannot possibly make one step in a straight, and a direct line. The earth itself being round, every step we make upon it, must necessarily be a segment, an arch of a circle. But yet though no piece of a circle be a straight line, yet if we take any piece, nay if we take the whole circle, there is no corner, no angle in any piece, in the entire circle. A perfect rectitude we cannot have in any ways in this world; in every calling there are some inevitable temptations. But, though we cannot make up our circle of a straight line (that is impossible to human frailty) yet we may pass on, without angles, and corners, that is, without disguises in our religion, and without the love of craft, and falsehood, and circumvention in our civil actions. A compass is a necessary thing in a ship, and the help of that compass brings the ship home safe, and yet that compass hath some variations, it doth not look directly north; neither is that star which we call the north-pole, or by which we know the north pole, the very pole itself; but we call it so, and we make our uses of it, as if it were so, because it is the nearest star to that pole. He that comes as near uprightness, as infirmities admit, is an upright man, though he have some obliquities. To God himself we may always go in a direct line, a straight, a perpendicular line; for God is vertical to me, over my head now, and vertical now to them, that are in the East, and West Indies; to our Antipodes, to them that are under our feet, God is vertical, over their heads, then when he is over ours.

Until about 1650 one gets an impression of the wholeness of the worlds of thought and nature in English literature. From the mid-century the gulf, which is the gulf between arts and sciences, becomes increasingly obvious. For a variety of reasons, principally, but not entirely, the growth of interest in science, English style was to grow simpler, less metaphorical, and less allusive, while the interest of writers was directed increasingly to good sense, rather than involved feelings.

Amongst the causes making for a simpler, less metaphorical style, was the experience of the Civil War. After 1660, Englishmen were exasperated with the idealists, the preachers of utopias, religious or otherwise. 'Enthusiasm', when it was not denounced as a cloak for political ambition, was derided as sheer lack of human balance. The Restoration of Charles II saw a great upsurge of worldliness as a reaction to the squabbling of the religious sects during the Commonwealth. It is said that Charles II ordered his preachers to keep their sermons short and to the point, having suffered much from the verbose and diffuse Presbyterian preachers while he was with the Scots, and this may have had its small effect in simplifying the language. The returning exiles carried with them a polished cynicism they had learned in France. A second stimulus to simplicity of expression was the great growth in public literacy in the seventeenth century. This was partly a response to the superb Authorized Version of the Bible; but many also learned to read to instruct themselves in astronomy for navigation, or mechanics for shipbuilding or the manufacture of watches, and had no wish for the pleasures of learned references to the Greek and Latin classics. (Something of the same process may be seen in the change in English style, particularly in newspapers, during the past hundred years, as once again there has been a 'literacy explosion'. Popular journalism has to cater for the nearmoron, and has effected a simplification of style generally.) Later seventeenth-century prose was often functional of necessity, for it was conveying precise facts to the self-educated artisan. But the most important influence was the conscious effort of the Royal Society itself.

Sprat, who in 1667 wrote the *History of the Royal Society*, thus described the favoured principles of prose style:

They have therefore been most rigorous in putting in execution the only remedy that can be found for this extravagance, i.e. this vicious abundance of phrase, the stricken metaphors, this volubility of tongue, which makes so great a noise in the world; and that has been, a constant resolution, to reject all the amplifications, digressions, and swellings of style; to return back to the primitive purity, and shortness, when men delivered so many things, almost in an equal number of words. They have exacted from all their members a close, naked, natural way of speaking;

positive expressions; clear senses; a native easiness: bringing all things as near the mathematical plainness, as they can; and preferring the language of artizans, countrymen, and merchants, before that, of wits or scholars.

In 1664, in fact, the Royal Society had set up a committee, with the conscious aim of modifying the English language; and this might have become an academy like the French Academy, had it not been that after three or four meetings the Society lost interest. The poets Dryden and Waller, and the diarist Evelyn, all writers of acknowledged distinction, served on the committee alongside members of more purely scientific interests.

One can already detect a changed attitude to literary analogy in *Paradise Lost* (1667), especially where, in Book V, Raphael is describing to Adam and Eve the revolt of Satan and his expulsion from Heaven. The analogy – for Raphael admits that his account is none other – is on a very conscious level, and the angel is very aware of the fact that he is giving spiritual truths a material clothing.

> Sad task and hard, for how shall I relate
> To human sense th'invisible exploits
> Of warring spirits; how without remorse
> The ruin of so many glorious once
> And perfect while they stood; how last unfold
> The secrets of another world, perhaps
> Not lawful to reveal? yet for thy good
> This is dispensed, and what surmounts the reach
> Of human sense, I shall delineate so
> *By likening spiritual to corporeal forms,*
> *As may express them best,* though what if Earth
> Be but the shadow of Heaven, and things therein
> Each to other like, more than on Earth is thought?

Earlier writers might have managed to describe a celestial war without such an apology. Later writers, Blake excepted, were unable to describe the eternal in material terms at all.

Milton himself lived on the watershed, as it were, between the two worlds. (He was able also to appeal to authority in the manner of a medieval writer, or to experimental research, as has been mentioned in a previous chapter, where he toys with the idea of gravitational attraction.)

It is of the conscious rejection of metaphor as anything more than a pretty ornament for verse that T. S. Eliot was speaking when he made his celebrated remark about the 'dissociation of sensibility' that sets in at this time in English poetry: henceforth there is a difference between the intellectual poet and the reflective poet. The early seventeenth-century poet, he said, was quite different from his nineteenth-century successor:

Tennyson and Browning are poets, and they think; but they do not feel their thought as immediately as the odour of a rose. A thought to Donne was an experience; it modified his sensibility. When a poet's mind is perfectly equipped for its work, it is constantly amalgamating disparate experience; the ordinary man's experience is chaotic, irregular, fragmentary. The latter falls in love, or reads Spinoza, and these two experiences have nothing to do with each other, or with the noise of the typewriter or the smell of cooking; in the mind of the poet these experiences are always forming new wholes.

The whole tide of opinion was running strongly against poetry, metaphor, and poetic prose. The philosophers generally saw them as an obstacle to truth. Hobbes regarded metaphor as one of the hindrances to straight thinking. Rousseau thought that the philosophy of Descartes had 'cut the throat of poetry'; and John Locke, late in the century, openly regarded poetry as made up of 'pleasant pictures and agreeable visions in the fancy', but basically misleading. Milton is the last poet to retain a certain wholeness of vision; and perhaps the last prose writer of the kind is Sir Thomas Browne.

Sir Thomas Browne (1606–82) was one of the interesting

transition figures one encounters in the study of the seventeenth century. He was a doctor who had studied in Oxford, Montpellier, Padua and Leyden, and who for forty-five years of his professional life lived at Norwich. His best-known works are *Religio Medici* (a doctor's religion), a sane and moderate plea for Anglicanism (published 1643), and *Hydriotaphia : Urn-Burial* (published 1658). A work which was important in its day was his *Pseudodoxia Epidemica, or Vulgar Errors* (1646), which corrected such common beliefs as that a man weighs heavier dead than alive, that salamanders live in the fire, that chameleons eat air, and that there is such a bird as the phoenix. However, he proclaimed his belief in the reality of witchcraft in *Religio Medici*, and went so far as to say that those who disbelieved in it were a species of atheist. Indeed, in 1664 his opinion was asked in a witchcraft case, and although the judge was inclined to acquit the two women accused, Browne's opinion helped to secure a conviction. Witchcraft trials were perhaps the ugliest of the institutions that the growth of science helped to sweep away, and it is a melancholy fact that Sir Thomas Browne, obviously a kindly and tolerant man, should have been almost the last distinguished participant in one. But in many ways, besides looking to the new, especially through experiment, Browne clung to the old; and it is interesting that he failed to gain admittance to the Royal Society, much as he would have liked to become a Fellow.

His interesting style, as well as his attitude to science, is admirably illustrated by *Urn-Burial*, a fascinating, slim, semi-scientific work which arose from the discovery near Walsingham, of forty or fifty burial urns, which he believed to be Roman. From a consideration of these urns, Browne goes on to reflect on the funeral customs of all nations, chiefly from literary evidence. But besides being a descriptive work, a piece, as it were, of comparative sociology, it is a religious meditation; he ends with the reflection that immortality is not to be gained through a sepulchre or monument, but through the Christian faith. Other religious references and comparisons are to be found on almost every page. That they are not obtrusive is because intellect and reflection are working unitedly. Disparate experiences naturally formed new wholes in Browne's mind. Readers who have a nostalgia for the time when scientific observations, classical learning, and moral reflection could form a harmonious whole, are delighted with such passages as the following:

How the bulk of a man should sink into so few pounds of bones and ashes, may seem strange unto any who considers not its constitution, and how slender a mass will remain upon an open and urging fire of the carnal composition. Even bones themselves reduced to ashes, do abate a notable proportion. And consisting much of a volatile salt, when that is fired out, make a light kind of cinders. Although their bulk be disproportionable to their weight, when the heavy principle of salt is fired out, and the earth almost only remaineth; observable in sallow, which maketh more ashes than oak; and discovers the common fraud of selling ashes by measure, and not by ponderation.

Some bones make best skeletons, some bodies quick and speediest ashes: who would expect a quick flame from hydropical Heraclitus? The poisoned soldier when his belly brake, put out two fires in Plutarch. But in the plague of Athens, one private pyre served two or three intruders; and the Saracens burnt in large heaps, by the King of Castile, shewed how little fuel sufficeth. Though the funeral pyre of Patroclus took up an hundred foot, a piece of an old boat burnt Pompey; and if the burthen of Isaac were sufficient for an holocaust, a man may carry his own pyre.*

This carefully weighed, conscious style, full of Latin and Greek loan-words, is the antithesis of what was favoured

---

* Browne's style helped to form that of Dr. Samuel Johnson, whose immense learning, critical acumen, and strong moral and religious sensibilities made it very well suited to him. But Browne has been admired, rather than imitated, by other great prose writers of later ages.

either by Hobbes ('you shall hardly meet with a senseless and insignificant word, that is not made up of some Latin or Greek names') or Sprat ('preferring the language of artizans, countrymen, and merchants'). They were interested in the development of prose style in accordance with the new mechanical concepts of natural philosophy. That the influence of the simplifiers prevailed, we owe in large measure to John Dryden.

Dryden constantly advocated, and used, this functional and unadorned prose, and it is not far from the truth to say that modern English is the language of Dryden. A brief example will suffice, taken from the preface to *Don Sebastian*, one of Dryden's last plays, first acted in 1690. He is explaining why he has not kept the 'Three Unities', that sacred cow of his times.

I must further declare freely, that I have not exactly kept to the three mechanic rules of unity. I knew them, and had them in my eye, but followed them only at a distance; for the genius of the English cannot bear too regular a play: we are given to variety, even to a debauchery of pleasure. My scenes are therefore sometimes broken, because my underplot required them so to be, though the general scene remains – of the same castle; and I have taken the time of two days, because the variety of accidents which are here represented could not naturally be supposed to arrive in one: but to gain a greater beauty, it is lawful for a poet to supersede a less.

Dryden declared that Latin loan-words ought to be used for effects of splendour only, and then sparingly. This is entirely in accord with modern practice, which prefers the simple Saxon word for everyday use, reserving the Latin or Greek for special effects (compare *fire* and *conflagration*), and makes Dryden's prose seem very modern compared with anything written before.

The eighteenth century was an age of reason, restraint and good breeding. It was very generally felt after Newton's

I

Principia had settled the heavens, and the Glorious Revolution had settled England and saved Europe, that law and order were needed in literature too. Edmund Waller and Dryden had led the way in the poetic concentration on 'smoothness of numbers', and polished heroic couplets came particularly into vogue. They tried to attain effects by the use of well-balanced thoughts, in moderate and appropriate language. Metaphors were admitted as an ornament, but not if they disturbed the reader's judgment, or swept him off his feet. As Pope says,

> True wit is nature to advantage dressed;
> What oft was thought, but ne'er so well expressed,

himself using a moderate, sane metaphor to say it. Addison, in *The Spectator*, was another preacher of moderation. He devoted several issues to differentiating betweeen True and False Wit, placing in the latter category all verse relying on verbal play alone, together with acrostics and other puzzles. True Wit, to Addison, was the skilful juxtaposition of sound ideas, so that the one illustrated the other.

An interesting result of this literary move towards good breeding, law and restraint, was that Aristotle, now scorned and rejected as a philosopher, became one of the legislators of the drama. Aristotle's *Poetics* was not, however, dependent on the rest of his works, for its value, and in fact its method, is rather inductive than deductive. As far as there could be a scientific treatment of dramatic method Aristotle had given it. In his *Essay on Criticism*, Pope urged the aspiring author to follow Nature (not the rugged, anarchic Nature of Wordsworth, but the unerringly law-abiding Nature of Newton). He *therefore* urges the writer to abide by the literary rules of the ancients:

> Those rules of old, discovered, not devised,
> Are nature still, but nature methodized:
> Nature, like liberty, is but restrained

> By the same laws which first herself ordained . . .
> Learn hence for ancient rules a just esteem;
> To copy Nature is to copy them.

One rule, however, was that the rules were not to be taken *too* rigidly:

> Great wits may sometimes gloriously offend,
> And rise to faults true critics dare not mend.

But in general Aristotle, Longinus, and Horace had laid down the laws by which successful poetry and drama was to be written; and in recent years the French critic Boileau had brought the whole system to perfection.

To see how the new spirit worked in practice, one may compare Shakespeare's *Antony and Cleopatra* with Dryden's treatment of the story in *All For Love*. Shakespeare's play is grand, diffuse, barbaric, moving from Rome to Alexandria and back, with occasional scenes in Parthia, Sicily and Greece, ranging over several years. Dryden's play, at a slight cost in historical accuracy, is set entirely in Alexandria, the events happening in one day dramatically, if not actually, the plot being tightly woven and very clever. The language is generally restrained, though it rises to heights on occasion. There is hardly a memorable line in the whole work, even though it is far from being a bad play.

The rise of prose in the eighteenth century, particularly the rise of the novel, was in part a recognition that there was a limit beyond which verse could not now aspire. There is much competent verse of the eighteenth century, but little that could be called first-rate. But while poetry is stagnant, the novel shows a steady gain in momentum. The emotional pitch appropriate to prose was more in keeping with the post-Newtonian century, and from its beginnings in the works of Swift and Defoe the novel becomes progressively stronger as the eighteenth century advances, until at the beginning of the nineteenth a high peak is reached in the work of Jane Austen. The long poems of the eighteenth century are, in contrast to the prose works, of only specialist interest, when they are of any interest at all, with the exception of Pope's works at the beginning of the century and Goldsmith's and Dr. Johnson's later on. In the seventeenth century it was possible for Milton to express the 'epic spirit' in *Paradise Lost*. When we search in the following age for an expression of the same spirit, it is to the great prose works that we look, particularly to Gibbon's *Decline and Fall of the Roman Empire*, rather than to Thomson's *Seasons* or Young's *Night Thoughts*. The reason, once again, is that restraint and good sense demanded that metaphors should be thought, not felt; and thought metaphors do not create powerful poetry. Prose depends far less for its effectiveness on imagery of any kind. As Sir Arthur Quiller-Couch says, with particular reference to eighteenth-century prose:

The strength of good prose resides . . . in the marshalling of argument, the orderly procession of paragraphs, the disposition of parts so that each finds its telling, its proper place; the adjustment of the means to the end; the strategy which brings its full force into action at the calculated moment and drives the conclusion home upon an accumulated sense of *justice*.

It might have seemed to the readers of Dr. Johnson's day that the reign of good breeding, reason, restraint and law, and of prose, would be perpetual. But towards the end of the century appears the protest of that strange figure, William Blake. (The word 'appears' is perhaps a misnomer for the way in which his works were published; the early editions, published by Blake himself, are excessively rare collectors' pieces.) Blake regarded the poet as the same kind of being as an ancient Hebrew prophet, and as he also cultivated obscurity, and had a rather eccentric (Swedenborgian) religious upbringing, his fulminations are by no means easy to follow. But there is no mistaking his detestation of the work of Bacon, Newton and Locke. In *Jerusalem* (1804) occurs the following passage:

> I see the Past, Present and Future existing all at once
> Before me. O Divine Spirit, sustain me on thy wings!
> That I may awake Albion from his long and cold repose;
> For Bacon and Newton, sheathed in dismal steel, their
>   terrors hang
> Like iron scourges over Albion. Reasonings like vast
>   serpents
> Infold around my limbs, bruising my minute articulations.
>
> I turn my eyes to the Schools and Universities of Europe
> And there behold the Loom of Locke, whose woof rages
>   dire,
> Washed by the Water-wheels of Newton: black the cloth
> In heavy wreathes folds over every nation: cruel works
> Of many wheels I view, wheel without wheel, with cogs
>   tyrannic
> Moving by compulsion each other, not as those in Eden,
>   which,
> Wheel within wheel, in freedom revolve in harmony and
>   peace.

Blake regarded as evil the authors of restrictive legal codes and mechanistic philosophies alike. His protests begin as early as 1788, and he may therefore be fairly claimed to anticipate the less far-reaching, but more effective, protests of Wordsworth. Blake sought to overthrow the mechanical world-picture and substitute something based on the emotions and the spiritual sense. Wordsworth, on the other hand, attempted to elude the compulsions of the mechanical view of nature by claiming the existence of a species of truth separate from the material truths described by men of science, a truth accessible to the poet, who can pass them on to the ordinary man.

The Romantic Movement may, in one sense, be regarded as a poetic reaction against Newtonian certainty, against the attitude of Hobbes, that man is basically a machine, against the high value placed on reason as opposed to emotion which so characterizes the age of Pope. In his *Preface* to the *Lyrical Ballads* (1800), Wordsworth asserts that there is a kind of truth accessible to man through the use of the intuition, and accessible to all men as men, whereas the discoveries of the chemist, the botanist or the mineralogist are restricted to a few only. What the poet *feels* to be true *is* true, especially in the moral field:

> Aristotle, I have been told, has said that poetry is the most philosophic of all writing: it is so: its object is truth, not individual or local, but general, and operative; not standing on external testimony, but carried alive into the heart by passion; truth which is its own testimony, which gives competence and confidence to the tribunal to which it appeals, and receives them from the same tribunal.

He says he was endeavouring, in these poems, to be 'tracing in them, truly though not ostentatiously, the primary laws of our nature: chiefly, as far as regards the manner in which we associate ideas in a state of excitement'. The subject is of less importance than the emotion: 'the feeling therein developed gives importance to the action and situation, and not the action and situation to the feelings.' The poet is especially concerned with values, says Wordsworth, and with the passions. His business lies

> with our moral sentiments and animal sensations, and with the causes which excite these; with the operations of the elements, and the appearances of the visible universe; with storm and sunshine, with the revolutions of the seasons, with cold and heat, with loss of friends and kindred, with injuries and resentments, gratitude and hope, with fear and sorrow.

Wordsworth calls on his readers to 'let Nature be your teacher'; but his is a wild, anarchic Nature, far different from Pope's. This Nature was a source of fruitful moral lessons:

> Nor deem I less that there are Powers
> *Which of themselves our minds impress;*
> That we can feed this mind of ours
> In a wise passiveness.

Impassioned metaphor was once again possible. It was a long time before science was to penetrate and analyse human thoughts and motivations; the poet could have it his own way, and interpret his feelings of well-being arising from a spring day in a remote Westmorland valley as the beneficent influence of occult powers, teaching him a modern equivalent of the Ten Commandments, and no one would say him nay, provided he kept his statements subjective.

Romanticism was, of course, a form of escapism. Wordsworth retreated into his own intuitions. Coleridge fled to the medieval and the fantastic. Keats retreated to the medieval and the classical worlds, while Shelley pursued fantastic philosophical ideals. The nearest expression of the epic impulse which this age produced was Wordsworth's *Prelude*, an effort to describe the poet's own emotional development, very far from Milton's intention to 'justify the ways of God to man'. Romanticism in poetry lasted from 1798 at least until the 1914–18 War; and some would claim that it is alive yet. Its final flowering, in the work of the 'Georgian poets', fills the older type of school poetry book, and gives successive generations of pupils the impression that poetry is a complete retreat from the workaday world, that it is a matter of rural nostalgia and a shunning of city life.

Novelists, since the rise of Romanticism, seem to have been better able than poets to keep abreast of the changing world, and to comment on it fully and adequately. They were not, of course, tied to metaphorical methods which could be regarded only as subjectively true, if true at all. Poets have had the choice between the eighteenth-century technique of lowering tension and treating metaphor and imagery merely as a toy, and the romantic technique of exalting them as high subjective truth, at the cost of deserting the everyday world. Post-1918 poets have, significantly, been showing tremendous interest in the poetry of the Metaphysicals, the last poets before the Great Intellectual Revolution, and clever verbal ambiguity is once again in fashion, for the first time since Addison condemned it. They have also been at pains to comment on the world of men, which means in England today the industrial urban setting. They try to combine intellectual pleasure once again with the æsthetic appeal which no poem can be without, and in this way to solve the problem which has now been with poets for three centuries: how to make their work significant, something more than an amusement for an idle hour or a source of pretty moral lessons for children.

It was, of course, more than the impact of the seventeenth-century Intellectual Revolution which produced problems for nineteenth-century poets. The development of science led to the Industrial Revolution, with its complex economic and social problems, with which the individual poet or thinker was less able to cope without highly specialized knowledge. Metaphor was still able to produce beauty, but the new manufacturing methods were producing goods. There was a constant temptation for the poet, or for the arts man generally, to retreat from the world of the matter-of-fact, to which he felt he could contribute little that anyone wanted, to a world of private fantasy.

Today may be seeing a reversal of a three-hundred-year-old trend. Arts and sciences have been getting farther apart ever since the Great Intellectual Revolution; but modern civilization seems to be able to find a productive use for almost any type of skill. The visual artist has long been associated with industrial production in Scandinavia, and is now often seen on the English factory floor. The press, radio, television and other new industries have demanded ever more specialists in words. Some people affect to despise either arts or sciences when put to a practical use. This is narrow. In the seventeenth century, science made its great advances largely under the stimulus of pressing practical problems. The arts, in past ages, have achieved their greatest heights during periods of involvement with the world, not of withdrawal from it. They may well do so again.

Index